A King Production presents…

Coke Like The 80s...

A Trilogy

Joy Deja King
Peter Mack

Cover concept by Joy Deja King

Editor: Jacqueline Ruiz, tinx518@aol.com

Library of Congress Cataloging-in-Publication Data; King, Deja Joy
Coke Like The 80s: a series/by Joy Deja King, Peter Mack
For complete Library of Congress Copyright info visit;

www.joydejaking.com Twitter: @joydejaking

A King Production

P.O. Box 912, Collierville, TN 38027

A King Production and the above portrayal logo are trademarks of A King Production LLC.

This Book is Dedicated To My:

Family, Readers and Supporters.
I LOVE you guys so much. Please believe that!!

A Mil' In The Hole Is Every Real Nigga Goal...

Coke Like The 80's
Rick Ross

A KING PRODUCTION

Coke Like The 80s...

A TRILOGY

Joy Deja King
Peter Mack

Chapter One

The Pick Up

"Be careful, baby. This feel funny."

Benzo Al remembered Roxanne's warning as he drove north on the 405 freeway. Beside him sat a black duffel bag containing three kilos of powder cocaine like a rich passenger.

Benzo exited the freeway at the quiet suburb of Chatsworth. The small business complex was not far into the city. He turned his dropped Silverado truck into the small parking lot, the chrome lips slipping from meaty tires, crunching gravel.

The industrial parking lot was empty that Sunday morning, except for the twin black Mercedes sedans framing the door to the quiet two-story office building. Benzo imagined that this place buzzed with smart corporate people during the week. After killing the powerful engine, his fingers gripped the bulky .45 caliber pistol stowed in the pocket of his hoodie. His stomach tingled with nervous energy, not unlike any other time before a drug transaction. He took a deep breath, shaking it off.

From the side of the building a small plain car emerged; a blonde lady behind the wheel. She never looked in Benzo's direction, instead her focus and speed was fast and steady. Never slowing down, she bounced into the side street and turned left in the direction of houses.

She must come this way often as a shortcut on her way home, Benzo thought to himself. The surroundings were serene and quiet, except for the sharp chirping of small birds darting from spindly trees behind him. An occasional horn could be heard coming from the busy boulevard on the other side of the building.

The splitting of horizontal blinds across a second floor window caught his attention. He steeled himself against the nervousness he felt. Taking in a deep breath, he grabbed the small duffel bag and exited the truck.

He sensed no movement or unusual activity as he reached the door. Not until he closed the door behind him did he realize he'd been holding his breath. The cool corridor smelled of pine. Empty offices lined both sides of the carpeted hallway.

"Up here," said a familiar voice from the top of the stairway to Benzo's left.

"Hey. What's up, Mitch," replied Benzo, meeting the tall blonde man for the second time; the first time having sold him one kilo of cocaine.

"You find it okay?" Mitch smiled, one front tooth crooked and chipped, belying the shiny slacks and sports coat. His shirt was opened at the top, revealing a thin gold chain.

"Yeh," Benzo said, easing up the stairs and standing next to Mitch. He just as tall, though he had broader shoulders.

Mitch smiled, gesturing towards another white man seated at a conference table. Benzo's heart thumped double, sensing an odd posture in the silent big man who extended his hand across the table.

"You remember Roger," Mitch said, before disappearing into a conference room. Benzo noted the roughness of Roger's hand, wary of the way his suit fit tightly around his muscular torso. "You ain't gonna be scared traveling with all this money?" Mitch asked, emerging from the room carrying a brown grocery bag.

Benzo forced a grin. He wanted to look into the conference room. He wanted to get up and go to the bathroom. Something didn't feel right.

"So, what we got here?" Mitch said, gesturing to the duffel bag Benzo had set on the table.

Benzo shook off his suspicion. After all, it was too late now. "What we agreed on," he replied.

"Three kilos of cocaine," Mitch said, as if for the record. This was two more than the first time.

Benzo was still not sure why Roxanne agreed to sell these dudes dope. *All money ain't good money,* he thought to himself. Benzo grit his teeth. A trickle of sweat fell from his armpit, making him squirm. Mitch lifted a brick of cocaine from the duffel bag and placed it on the table.

"I'd be afraid to ride alone with all this dope," Roger said, speaking for the first time as Mitch stabbed the brick of dope with a pocketknife.

"I'm just an average citizen," replied Benzo.

"You ain't average, brother," Mitch said, smacking his lips with the taste of cocaine on his tongue. "And this ain't average dope."

Benzo was ready to leave. "Is that 45?" he asked, nodding towards the money.

"Yep." Mitch smiled. "Wanna count it?"

Benzo stood up, prepared to lay the cocaine on the table and scan count the money as he put it in the duffel bag.

"Could you come down to ten each if I buy more than three?" Mitch wanted to know. Benzo was reluctant to answer, not surprised by this inquiry. He reminded himself to question Roxanne on where she knew Mitch from. "I'll let you know," he said after a pause.

"The final decision ain't yours?" chimed in Roger, suddenly full of conversation.

"I'll let y'all know," Benzo said, hoisting the duffel bag on his shoulder.

"We'll be in touch," Mitch said to Benzo's back as he descended the stairs. Benzo shook off the ominous tone of the white man as he opened the door leading to the parking lot.

His first thought was, *Why is the familiar blonde lady walking up to me?* Then he saw the gun rising in her hand. *She wasn't takin' no shortcut,* he realized as more white people emerged from the edges of his sight. They were all shouting, guns pointed at him.

He saw Mitch and Roger exiting the building as he was being ushered into a waiting car, a sly grin on their faces as they were congratulated by their fellow pigs. Benzo caught Mitch's eyes through the milling throng of pigs. He regreted not following his instincts, instead satisfying Roxanne's wishes, even though she'd warned him to be careful.

Mitch strode over to the car, opening the door. He was all pig in demeanor and posture now. "You want my help,

Benzo?" he asked. "Cooperate with us. Give us Roxanne. Get us her connection. You walk from this car right now."

Benzo remained silent, wishing he could close the door himself. In reply, he leaned back and looked straight ahead.

Chapter Two

Who's To Blame

"Malik!"

He heard his mother call his name, but he couldn't move. He couldn't answer. He was weighed down by an invisible force that also sapped his air.

"Malik." A softer, more gentle voice. It was closer, having been awakened from sleep by his mother's harsher voice. He struggled to awaken; to escape the heavy force sitting like an elephant on his chest. He felt his body being nudged.

"Baby, wake up," said the urgently soft voice beside him.

He could feel the bed beneath him. He could feel

Trinity move her hands beneath the covers. They were warm against his lean torso and muscled stomach. Her fingers slipped beneath the band of his boxers and fondled his flaccid meat before gripping it to stroke.

Malik grunted, being pulled from his hazy nightmare of heavy nothingness. He was thankful for this assistance. He imagined that his mother would be calling him again soon.

Being lifted to wakefulness by the gentle stroking of his dick, he tried to figure what might be the reason for his mother's calling.

"Is that better, baby?" asked Trinity, gripping his hardness as she looked to his shuttered eyes, marveling at the long dark lashes.

The warmth of her mouth brought him to the surface of wakefulness. His dick pulsed as she took him deep inside her mouth. He groaned, his body tensing with the sensation of her gentle suctioning.

"Malik. Your granddaddy out here waiting on you," said his mother, her urgent voice just outside his bedroom door.

"He got time. Let him be," came the faint reply of his grandfather, no doubt seated in his favorite chair watching television.

"He needs to learn some responsibility. Did Trinity go home last night?"

Malik could imagine his mother rushing towards the front door, not expecting an answer from her father. She had done her part. Malik then remembered agreeing to take his grandfather to work so he could use his car for the day. He lifted his eyelids as Trinity gripped his dick tightly in her mouth, obviously sensing that he would be getting up shortly. Lazily, he stared down the length of his body as she sucked his dick, making it disappear inside of her mouth over and over again.

"Good morning, baby," Trinity said, turning to him briefly, smiling around the stiff meat in her mouth.

Malik grinned, whispering, "Good morning," as she returned to her mission. Her signature tongue swirl move around the base of his dick made his body jerk. This encouraged her, not long after, to pull from him the treasure she sought.

Malik exhaled with his spent energy as Trinity rose up from his lap. "Thought that would help," she said with a satisfied grin.

"Tell my G I'm coming," Malik said as Trinity pulled on a t-shirt that stopped just below her ass. "He gonna want some of that you go out there like that."

She smiled, stopping at the door. "Don't hate," she said before leaving the room.

Malik heard her greet his grandfather with a good morning on her way to the bathroom. He stretched hard, his 6'3" frame extending beyond the foot of the twin bed. He turned his pager on. It bubbled to life with missed messages.

After reaching for the phone on the nightstand, Malik unknots the coil while pressing out his homeboy's number.

"What's up, homie," Malik said.

"Nothin' much. You must got T over there. Gettin' up all late."

"Yeh. I'm finna be up though. Taking G'Pop to work."

Walking into the room, Trinity heard the last of his conversation. "Am I going with you?" she wanted to know.

"Shoota said, 'hi'," Malik said, more to ease any suspicion she might've had that he could be talking to a girl for the way she announced herself coming into the room.

"Hi," she replied, waving dismissively. "Am I going?"

"If you want to."

"Tell her ass to go home. She done already gave up the pussy," Shoota said into Malik's ear.

"We gon' get breakfast," Malik said to Trinity, but more for Shoota's benefit. Trinity smiled and bounced a new delight to get dressed in a pair of Calvin Klein jeans.

"Awww shit, nigga," complained Shoota. "Y'all going to Magic Mountain after that?"

Malik chuckled. "Naw."

Trinity looked his way sharply. "Oh, he got jokes? He better not be talking smack about me."

"Check with you later, dog," Malik said, recognizing Trinity's annoyance. He placed the phone in its cradle slowly. "What G doing?" he asked her.

"Waiting on us," replied Trinity with a satisfied grin.

By the time Malik got dressed his grandfather was sitting on the porch. He resembled a sharecropper for the way his slender, tall frame hid under a pair of jean overalls. He would be perfect with a corncob pipe in his hand. His small afro was a helmet of tightly knotted gray hair. His dark brown eyes were framed with a gray halo, looking out of a black face weathered by over 80 years of living.

"Ready to roll, G?" Malik said, looking out on to the block.

Across the street, Dutch was standing on his porch, surrounded by his sharply dressed friends while his mother measured him for what was surely to be a stylish shirt. Dutch and his friends were all wearing long, flowing perms, their hair dropping onto their shoulders in smooth waves.

Dutch's black '65 Chevy SS sat under a tarp in the front yard. At the curb sat his friends' shiny cars with Dayton spoke wire rims, giving them a look of ballerinas on precious chrome feet.

Malik's grandfather made his way to the Lincoln Continental parked in the driveway.

"I'm riding in the back, Mr. Toole," said Trinity, opening the rear door.

"Drugs gon' ruin the lot of 'em," grumbled Mr. Toole as Malik pulled into the street.

"Ain't nobody forcing nobody to do drugs, Mr. Toole," Trinity said.

"They sellin' it. That's enough."

"What drugs they selling, G?" Malik asked, amused by his grandfather's irritation.

Mr. Toole looked toward Malik sharply. "You don't know?" he quipped.

"They selling weed. That ain't never hurt nobody," Trinity inserted from the back seat, catching Malik's warning look through the rearview mirror.

"Somebody broke off my antennae," complained Mr. Toole. "Tryna make one of them crack pipes!"

Trinity hooted with laughter.

"What you know about crack pipes, G?" Malik asked, forcing a straight face.

"I ain't get to be this old without knowing what's what. Remember, I work around the most gossiping people on earth."

Malik nodded. He couldn't imagine what his grandfather heard at the beauty shop. The thought made him wonder how he stayed silent about what he knew about the streets and people's business.

"Mr. Toole be knowing what's up," said Trinity, smiling at Malik in the mirror.

Malik pulled to a stop at a red light. Next to him was a lowered Nissan truck, the bed filled with speakers, blaring Kurtis Blow. The man behind the wheel looked over with a stone-faced stare, his jheri curl hanging long over his shirt collar.

"Miss Ethel, down the street there," began Mr. Toole, "her son walked their television right out the house. He traded it for crack."

Malik pulled away, thinking that the Nissan driver must've sold cocaine. He looked too young to afford a brand new truck with all that music. The multi-colored gold flake paint job alone probably cost more than the Lincoln.

"Young boys got more money than they know what to do with. Little girls running right after 'em," complained Mr. Toole.

"People gonna do drugs no matter what. That's they problem," said Trinity.

Malik regretted letting her come. He doesn't look at her through the mirror. "G," he began, "you ever smoked weed or anything?"

Mr. Toole remained silent until they pulled into a parking spot outside of Jack's Family Kitchen on Western Avenue, across the street from Malik's elementary school.

"I got hooked on opium fighting oversees," he admitted, opening the door and shutting it on Malik's surprised expression.

"He was in the Army?" Trinity asked.

"Yep," replied Malik shortly before exiting the car.

Mr. Toole was spry for an old man. He reached the restaurant door while Malik and Trinity rush to catch up.

There was a spirited debate raging in the small, intimate diner. Mr. Toole slid into his favorite booth by the juke box, the beauty shop next door within sight. Malik and Trinity join him.

"Mark my words," said a chubby man wearing a mechanic's uniform. "It's the C.I.A."

"That's a conspiracy!" shouted another man, slim, and wearing a flannel shirt.

"Ain't no way the government selling drugs."

"Ha!" shouted the mechanic. "You must be a Republican. Jack! You let people who vote for Ronald Reagan eat in here?"

Jack looked up from the well of the kitchen alcove, his

head shaking as he tended to the grill. A chorus of laughter followed this accusation. The mechanic was emboldened.

"I can never understand how a black man can be a Republican. How you do that, Charles?" asked the mechanic.

"Easy," replied the flannel shirt wearing man. "Business. Black folk need to start doing for themselves. Stop relying on welfare."

"Ain't that some shit!" shouted a woman seated at the counter, nursing a cup of coffee. "It's more white folks on welfare because it's more of them. And if you think the government ain't capable of flooding our streets with dope then you the dumbest Uncle Tom ever!"

Another chorus of laughter filled the room. The debate continued, someone pointing out that Ronald Reagan was the governor and that he knew first hand where the dope could be sold. Someone else pointed out that he was responsible for stopping summer school free lunches and after school programs. This seemed to be enough to sway the room into believing he could be responsible for the drugs suddenly available in the city of Los Angeles.

Chapter Three

Roxanne... Roxanne

Roxanne tried to shake the butterflies in her stomach. It was only when she didn't act on her instincts that something went wrong. And she felt something had gone wrong.

"Mommy! Mommy!" called her seven-year-old son from the opened door of the car.

She looked to him, startled, awakened from her thoughts. Jasper stood outside the car, waiting to close the door. She hadn't realized he'd gotten out.

"I'm sorry, baby. You have your lunch?" she asked, waving to a smiling teacher passing with a throng of uniformed students.

Jasper hoisted his backpack onto his shoulder. "Yes, mom, but this just a snack. You said you were going to bring me McDonald's."

Marcus Garvey elementary school was one of the best private schools in Los Angeles. The tuition was worth seeing her second grade son successfully doing algebra and reading at an advanced level.

"Yes, J. If I can get away from the salon I'll bring you lunch."

Jasper screwed up his face, prepared to whine.

"Don't start that. I said I'll try. The cafeteria ain't bad. Shit, I pay enough for you to eat lunch here."

"No cursing, Mom."

Roxanne smiled. "Give Mommy a kiss," she said, leaning towards the opened passenger door.

"Mom, you're embarrassing me," he complained before giving her a light kiss on the cheek.

Roxanne leaned up with a smile as her son shut the door and scampered across the parking lot, disappearing inside the green building painted with a mural of dark skinned children at various forms of study and play.

A quick left on Slauson and a right on Crenshaw began the late morning drive to her beauty salon on Western Avenue. *Maximum Roxy* was the premier beauty salon for the latest women's hairstyles. Roxanne prided herself on keeping her clients up to date and fresh with the latest braids, tints, and feathers.

Roxanne uncradled her car phone and paged Benzo Al, wondering why she hadn't heard from him by now. He'd been scheduled to meet a new connect who had increased his purchase by thirty thousand dollars. It was hard to turn that down even though she had had reservations. She'd agreed only because Mitch came with a good reference.

She grabbed the ringing phone, anticipating that Benzo's voice would come through, calming her fears. "Hello?"

"Wassup, Roxy," said a feminine voice of authority. "You sound like you waiting on a lost puppy."

Roxanne relaxed, forcing the worry from her emotions. "Hey, Pearl. What's up?"

"Shit. Trying to be on your level. What's up with that two piece chicken dinner?"

"Is that for today? I completely forgot."

There was a moment of silence before Pearl said, "You slipping Roxy. We do straight business. No shenanigans."

Roxanne was reluctant to promise delivery since she hadn't heard from Benzo. She hoped to buy time by claiming she forgot, though she felt bad about it.

"You're right, Pearl. I'm sorry. Things have just not been right this morning. I promise to make it up to you."

"How you gonna do that... throw in a free biscuit or something?" asked Pearl, her dark laughter crackling through the phone line.

"Or something," replied Roxanne, making a right on Western, her salon in sight.

"Okay. Well, we ain't got no food in the cabinets. Lemme know something before I gotta go to Arby's or whatever."

Roxanne pulled to a stop in her parking space before the door of her salon, noting Mr. Toole's Lincoln only a few feet away across the small parking lot.

"Okay. Let me set something up. It's gonna probably be for tomorrow."

Pearl exhaled with irritation. "So, you got me for sure tomorrow? Them Arby's don't be right all the time."

Roxanne allowed herself to laugh softly to lighten the mood. "I hear you. Let me put something together for you."

"That'll work. Get at me." Roxanne assured Pearl that

she would before getting out the car. Mr. Toole was walking in her direction, Malik and Trinity heading towards the car.

"You can't speak, Malik?" called out Roxanne.

Mr. Toole looked back as if noticing his grandson for the first time. "Don't be rude, boy. Come on over here and say hi," he said, working a toothpick between his teeth. Roxanne ignored the irritated look on Trinity's face as Malik peeled away to walk across the gravel her way.

"Damn, Malik! If you were over 18 I might have to steal you for a night," joked Roxanne, grinning more than necessary, flashing gold-framed teeth.

Malik responded, "I'll be 18 next summer."

"So, what you doin' with yourself... you play basketball or something?"

Malik hesitated, shyness overtaking him.

"Go 'head and tell 'er boy. She might be able to help you," said his grandfather.

"I was talking to a few college teams. USC was looking at me."

"Oh, that's cool. You got skills?"

Malik grinned. He tried not to stare at the diamond rings on her fingers. The cleavage of her breasts were filled with the many gold necklaces hanging from her neck. Everything about her said money. Her hair was whipped and feathered with a burgundy tint, matching the color of her Nissan Maxima.

"That sounds cool. Maybe you can play for the Lakers with Magic," she said.

"They told the boy he need to attend basketball camp, but he think he ready just like he is," chimed in Mr. Toole.

"Can't nobody hold me," Malik said proudly.

"He too lazy to work for it. He don't know what's good don't come free and easy," added Mr. Toole, continuing his stride toward the front of the salon, separating a key from a large ring of keys to open the front door.

"You gotta pay for camp?" asked Roxanne.

"Yeh, but I don't need that," replied Malik, his eyes sliding over her shapely hips wrapped tight in designer jeans.

The sudden honking of a horn interrupted their conversation. Trinity was impatient, looking at them through the back window of the Lincoln.

"Oh, excuse me," exclaimed Roxanne. "I think your little girlfriend needs you."

"Malik," called Mr. Toole. "Make sure you put some oil in the car. And don't bring it back without gas!"

Malik had $20 in his pocket. He was reluctant to ask for money in front of Roxanne.

"What time you want me to come pick you up?" he asked his grandfather.

"Not long after nine. Gotta fix a hair dryer later."

Roxanne smiled, deep dimples denting her chocolate skin. "He's so handy," she said just as the horn honks again. "She is too much. You better go before she come get you," advised Roxanne, her brown eyes twinkling.

"Alright," said Malik, turning from the jeweled hairstylist. "See you later."

"You should think about basketball camp some more. Don't waste your opportunity," she said to him before he could turn and walk away. She thought to herself what a nice smile he had just as the horn honks again.

Mr. Toole had turned on all the lights and prepared her favorite work station for special clients. She was about to compliment him on how nice Malik was when the ringing office phone grabbed her attention.

Roxanne was huffing when she picked up the phone, after having trotted through the salon to the rear office.

"Maximum Roxy," she answered. "Roxanne speaking."

"Good morning, Roxy."

She knew who it is before he could announce himself. "Hi, Saul. Please don't give me any bad news," she said to her long time criminal defense attorney.

"I'm sorry to be the bearer of bad news," he said. "Benjamin was arrested this morning in Chatsworth."

Roxanne let out a deep sigh as she plopped down in the chair behind her desk. Her suspicions had been proven correct.

"Roxanne?"

She blinked hard, tearing her eyes away from Mr. Toole as he watered the plants around the salon through the one-way mirror.

"Yes. I'm here," she replied, a sense of dread spreading over her. "Does he have a bail?"

"Unfortunately not. We'll have a bail hearing after he's processed. No later than Friday."

The silence grew pregnant between them before Roxanne asked, "Did he have anything else to say?"

"Yeh. Told me to let you know the hill ain't good." This was what she was afraid of. Mitch was referred to her by Hill. Now the question was does Hill know of Benzo's arrest.

"Anybody arrested with him?" she asked, wondering if Mitch could be a cop.

"He didn't say. Just wanted to give you that message. I'll go see him tomorrow. So, drop by my office and we'll discuss our next move."

Roxanne took a deep breath, calculating her losses and obligations. "Thanks, Saul. See you tomorrow." Roxanne hung up and called Hill's pager, leaving her number behind.

Chapter Four

Taste Of The Game

"Why you had to be all up on her like that?" asked Trinity, having repeated this question many times since they'd left the salon.

"Come on, baby. My mom gonna be home in a minute," Malik responded, advancing on her, pushing her flailing arms to the side.

"Naw naw, Malik. Back up."

"That lady is my G'Pop boss. Why you tripping? She called me over there."

She looked up at him from the bed, having backed up

and fallen to a sitting position. "Now you tryna be all up on me." She pouted. "You act like you can't see what I see."

Malik grinned, thinking her jealousy was cute. "What you see?"

She stared at him, her gray eyes sparkling. Her light brown cheeks had blossomed crimson.

"Don't be like that. You know ain't nobody for me but you," he assured her, leaning to kiss her, avoiding her protests until she gave in.

"I ain't playin' with you," she said, stopping to look into his eyes.

Malik nodded, agreeing.

He returned his lips to hers, easing her back to the mattress. He caressed her thighs, pushing up her sheer skirt. He kissed her neck, shoulder, and breasts. Trinity felt his growing meat press against her through his basketball shorts. Her legs opened to receive him between her thighs. She grinded with him as he wedged himself within her embrace. Malik pulled his erect joint over the rim of his shorts and pulled her panties to the side. Her wetness caught his breath as she pulled him inside her. He lowered himself to her and relaxed inside of her warmth.

Trinity exhaled sweetly against his neck as he slid in and out of her, the friction bringing her to hot heights of pleasure. She held him in her embrace, bringing him deeper inside her, gripping him tightly in want of his explosion.

"Oh, baby," gasped Trinity, heat gathering at her center. Malik grunted, long stroking her, watching himself slide in and out, her wetness making his joint shiny black.

"Give it to me," she urged, grabbing his swollen meat in her walls. Malik trapped her breast in his mouth, his tongue circling the swollen nipple as he stroked her faster.

"Yes!" Trinity cried out, scratching along his back.

"Malik!" his mother called out, knocking on the

bedroom door.

Malik seizes up, his orgasm interrupted. "Oh, shit!" he hissed, pulsing inside of Trinity.

"Did you put oil in the car?"

Malik collapsed onto Trinity, breathing heavily.

"Damn, baby. She gets on my nerves," complained Trinity.

"Malik! You need to send your girlfriend home and make sure you put oil in the car!"

"Gawwd! You need to get your own place," said Trinity.

Malik's pager beeped, giving him an excuse to ignore her comments about his mother and getting his own place.

"Who is that?" she wanted to know, jumping from the bed.

Malik moved the pager from her grasping hands. "Why you tripping, girl? Back up."

"Oh, I can't see who paging you now?" She stood defiant as he picked up the telephone.

Malik ignored her, speaking into the phone. "What's up, homie," he said, watching her stare him down. "That sound cool. I gotta get G in a few though." Trinity grabbed her purse.

"Come scoop me up." Malik waited for her question after he hung up the phone.

"Where you going?" she wanted to know, watching him search for a pair of pants.

"Hit Crenshaw real quick."

Trinity smacked her lips. "Ain't nothin' on the 'Shaw but car-hops. You better not be talking to no skanks," she warned, shoving the side of his head with her finger tips. Malik grinned with her playful nudge, glad that she didn't carry on with her antics to forbid him to go.

"Call me when you get back," she said, waiting at the bedroom door for his agreement. He was reluctant to agree, but did so anyway so as not to halt her leaving. Shoota was waiting for him at the curb in his primered '78 Cutlass on laces and twenties. Malik felt like a gang member every time he rode with Shoota, though neither one of them were.

"That nigga Dutch just got at me," said Shoota when Malik got in the car. "He gonna serve me some double-up."

"For real?" replied Malik. "I ain't never seen him sell crack."

"He only fuck with a select few," Shoota said proudly. "I'm just gonna get a few crackheads to serve to. Maybe open up a spot." Malik could see the gleam of coming riches in Shoota's eyes. They had been friends since elementary school. Shoota had always been the more daring.

"I'll still blam a nigga, but I'm trying to be more playa about mines," said Shoota, adjusting the large gun in his lap.

"You still might have to shoot these fools over crack," warned Malik, looking over at his friend as they headed down Vernon Avenue towards Crenshaw.

Sunday nights on Crenshaw were special, but even on a week night the boulevard was alive with eager women, lurking jackers, and nice cars driven by the hood reputables of the city. Driving down the 'Shaw could be like touring an amusement park or being an eyewitness to someone's tragedy.

Traffic was light as Shoota made a left on Vernon, riding up Crenshaw towards Slauson. "Look," said Shoota, nodding towards the expanded sidewalk along a wall mural.

Gleaming low-riders with candy paint sitting on gold Daytons crowded the mini-street off the boulevard. On the sidewalk sharply dressed men surrounded a tall man with giant Turkish ropes hanging from his neck.

"That's Freeway Rick," said Shoota, growing silent as the rich group fades.

"We can't be out here too long," said Malik, eyeing a group of smiling girls in a Toyota Tercel next to them. They all wore the popular basket weave hairstyle, with large gold hoops hanging from their ears.

"Naw. I just need to check on a few things," responded Shoota.

This got Malik's attention. Shoota always had something going on that he only shared when it was sometimes too late to refuse participation.

"What you mean?"

"Remember that double-up I was telling you about?"

"Yeh." Malik was wary. He was reminded of something his grandfather told him; *If you don't make plans someone else will make them for you.*

"This nigga Hill be buying ounces. Dutch say he give me a ounce of powder cocaine for six hundred. I'm gonna see what Hill get his for."

"What about the double-up rocks?" asked Malik.

"If Hill get his for more than I'll pocket the change and get my double-up for free," replied Shoota, grinning with his scheme.

Malik shook his head, thinking how much risk was involved to save a few dollars.

"There he go right there," said Shoota, looking to a black '79 Coupe with the tail jacked in the air. It was going in the other direction.

Shoota bumped the horn, getting the driver's attention. He waved, motioning Hill to the Shell gas station parking lot where several shiny cars were already congregated with groups of people. No one appeared to be getting gas.

Hill busted a U-turn and met them at the gas station, pulling alongside them so that he was next to Shoota, facing the opposite direction.

"What's up, loc," said Hill, looking like a mix of Mexican and Black, his black wavy hair tied in a loose braid at the back of his head.

"What's up with y'all," replied Shoota. "Wassup, Al?" he added to the similar looking man in the passenger seat. He nodded.

Hill kept his dark eyes moving, scanning the gas station and the street beyond.

"What you got?" he asked.

"What you get your ounces for?"

"Powder or rocked up?" asked Hill.

"Both."

"Powder for six. Rocked up I get for three fifty. Why, you trying to cop?"

"Naw," replied Shoota, disappointment in his voice. "I'm trying to get some myself. Just looking for a cool price."

"How much you trying to spend?" Hill wanted to know.

Shoota stalled, looking over to Malik. "You wanna go in together?"

Malik shrugged. "I'm tapped out," he said, happy that he was. He didn't trust Hill at first sight.

"I'm just tryna get a double up fifty. Something small to start off with."

Al chuckled from the passenger seat. He whispered something to Hill, who leaned under the seat and brought up a baggy of rock cocaine. "Gimme a hundred dollars for that," he said, handing the baggy to Shoota. "Thas ten twenties in there. You can make 'em smaller, but I wouldn't."

Shoota handed the baggy to Malik. "All I got is fifty right now," he said to Hill.

"That's cool. You owe me fifty," he replied, taking the money. "Ey, you know a nigga name Benzo?"

Shoota frowned as if in thought. He'd heard the name before, but couldn't say that he knew Benzo personally. "Naw. Why?"

Hill's attention was already elsewhere. "No reason. Thought you might know him," he said, taking his foot off the brake. "Hit me up tomorrow," he added, gliding away and turning onto Crenshaw.

Malik massaged the bag of rocks, feeling its power. *This is a start to basketball camp*, he thought to himself.

A series of cracking sounds interrupted what Shoota was about to say. They both looked towards the firecracker sounds. The group of women surrounding a convertible Mustang on gold Dayton wire rims were clearing the scene.

A group of masked men had jumped out of a white Caprice Classic with guns. They shot the driver of the Mustang, leaving him bleeding between the gas pumps. One of them jumped into the Mustang and peeled off.

Malik looked upon the carnage transfixed as Shoota slammed down on the gas and followed the Mustang onto Crenshaw, turning in the opposite direction.

Chapter Five

Streets Be Talkin'

The Law Offices of Saul Benjamin lay nestled between an Oriental Noodle shop and a nail shop on Vermont Avenue, just past Wilshire. Korea Town. Saul Benjamin had the look of a man who'd spent long stretches in hot, steamy countries, swindling, conning, and cajoling wealth.

Roxanne parked in a small graveled lot behind the narrow office building. Her gold flake, burgundy pearl paint flashed like a gem among the mostly black luxury sedans around her. The smell of nail cleaner and eggs mixed in the narrow walkway to the front. After Roxanne announced herself to the petite Korean receptionist, she stood by, not expecting to wait.

"Roxanne," Saul said somberly, opening a door to the left of the receptionist. His stomach pressed tightly against a pair of leather suspenders. His face was flush and fleshy.

Roxanne returned his greeting, concerned for his health. "You see a doctor lately?" she asked, striding to a leather straight-backed chair before his too small desk.

Saul cleared his throat with a gurgle. "The government poisoned me. Which one I don't know," he replied, striding with big arcing steps to his desk chair.

"Give me the business, Saul," said Roxanne, adjusting her Cazal glasses.

Saul splayed his fleshy pink palms between them. "He's fucked. At least for now. He refused to cooperate."

"Cooperate?!" She stared deathly serious at Saul. "Cooperate with you?" she asked, gold bangles jangling on her wrists with the sudden movement of her arms.

"The feds," Saul responded, now pressing his palms together. "They want you and your connect. They suspect it's Mario Peña, friend of your son's father."

Roxanne peered into Saul's ocean blue eyes, almost asking him if she should leave the country.

"He's not cooperating," Saul repeated. "He said that to play Hill for a minute. Keep him close. Says don't make any moves." Roxanne sat still, eyeing Saul, uncomfortable with him expecting that she would follow orders from Benzo.

Roxanne took a slow breath before she asked, "What can I expect at his bail hearing?"

"Currently, he has no bail," said Saul, then adding with a rock of his head, "criminal history, organized crime... yada yada yada."

He's not cooperating, she thought to herself. "Can you get a bail for him?"

27

He nodded. "Sure can. Five million dollars."

"Will there be questions about where the money comes from?"

Saul grinned, exposing a gold cap on his left canine tooth. "For forty percent I can get him out. No questions. The equity comes from a shell company."

One million for bail and one million to this sheisty muthafucka, she thought to herself. *I'd have five million cash if not for you promising to get my husband off death row.*

"Okay," she said, reaching into her Louis Vuitton purse and pulling out a fluffy envelope. "I need his bail lower. A lot lower," she added.

Saul cracked open the envelope and thumbed the money. He shook his hand, letting it fall to the desk. "Let's see what happens," he said.

Roxanne wanted to persist, but was quietly thankful for Saul. He held all her secrets. She couldn't be mad at him for wanting to be paid for his services. It was when she made that right on Manchester off Vermont that she realized her money was short. There was no way she could sit still and expect to live in fashion; not to mention get Benzo's bail money. *But first things first,* she said to herself as she made a right down West Boulevard.

These Inglewood streets were familiar to her. They raised her. It was where she fell in love with her husband. The man on death row for killing a DEA agent; specifically for planning, organizing, and paying someone else to do it, except no one knew who actually did it.

Hill's house represented the center of Rolling 60s Crips, where Hyde Park intersected West Boulevard. It is a ramshackle affair on a dirt lot. A rusted red '52 Ford truck sat idle in the driveway, which openly led to a leaning garage. The black Cadillac Coupe sat at the curb like a waiting menace, its tail jacked up. Hill bounded down the rickety steps, kicking up dust from the cement walkway.

"What's up, cuz?" said Hill, leaning to the open passenger window.

"Get in," replied Roxanne, turning off the motor.

Roxanne noted that the blue khaki pants he was wearing could be the same ones she saw him wearing two weeks ago, when he'd asked her to do him a favor. Mitch was his stolen auto fence, so he'd claimed. He needed to buy a bird. More the next time. Roxanne didn't like new clients, but Hill rarely asked for favors and he was someone you wanted to keep on your good side.

"Benzo locked up," she said, holding up a palm to combat the surprised look and impending question of, "When? How?"

She wanted to answer his unasked question with, "*Nigga, you know who,*" but instead she said, "He went to meet your boy Mitch. He's a fed." She held up her hand to stop his mock protest.

"I'm not here to accuse you of anything or question you about anything."

Hill relaxed in his seat, leaned back, and eyed her sideways.

"I'm just here to let you know what happened," she added.

"That's crazy," Hill finally muttered, shaking his head. "So, Benzo locked up."

Roxanne caught him looking to her suddenly, as if caught sneaking. "I might need to call on you. I need to know you'll be there for me," she said, sure now that Hill knew Mitch was a fed.

Hill agreed, nodding one time. "I got you," he said, not trusting his speech.

It was all she could do, she felt. The best thing to do. Wear a velvet glove. Benzo had that part right. Keep him close. But there was no way she'd stay still. Roxanne was further resolved in this, calculating her next move on her way to the salon. First thing was find someone trustworthy to run her dope.

Maximum Roxy was oddly dim. She checked her Cartier watch. Nearly noon. She exited the car and peered through the painted window. *Where is Mr. Toole?* she wondered, reaching for her key.

The crunch of gravel got her attention, creeping under the lowering base and rhymes of Kool Moe Dee. The cracking pebbles gnawed near her ankles, the front tire of a giant wheel stopping too close.

The roof had been replaced with a retractable canvas Flintstone top. The emerald green paint was topped with intricate brightly colored strokes awash with gold flake. Two candy paint '64 Chevy low-riders stop in the narrow driveway behind this neon metal crib.

"Waddup, Rox," said Freeway Rick, smiling from the high passenger seat.

"Hey, Ricky," replied Roxanne, waiting for it. She believed the rumor that he got his cocaine from the C.I.A.

"Tell Benzo to call me if he need me," he said.

Bad news travels fast, she thought to herself. "His bail is five million." She watched for a break in Freeway's easy grin. It only turned serious.

Freeway nodded. "We might be able to work something out," he said, smiling bigger now. "You ready to come on home?"

Roxanne was shaking her head before she could say, "I'm cool."

He lifted his arms to the city. "It's a big world out here. You playing in the yard," he said.

Roxanne opened the front door. "Have a good day, Ricky," she responded. "Send your girlfriends here to get their hair done."

Freeway chuckled as she stepped into the salon. "I just might do that," he said to the closing front door.

"Shit!" she hissed to herself once in the salon, her heart beating light and fast.

Turning on lights as she went, thoughts of sharks in water invaded her mind. Once in the office she reached for the phone to call Mr. Toole at home. He didn't carry a pager.

The phone rang just as she reached to press the first number. "Maximum Roxy," she answered.

"This Al. You good?" said Benzo.

Roxanne was both glad and shocked to hear his voice. "I saw Saul. We good," she said, hoping he didn't get curious of details. No way should he or could he expect to get bailed out, but chiefly, no way did she follow orders from him.

"Cool." Benzo was silent for a beat before he said, "I appreciate you hiring Saul for me."

"Oh, that's all you playboy. I put that away from what we get together for times like this."

"That's smart," he offered, the line pregnant with an unasked question.

"Now, you ain't been working long enough to have five million in the kitty," she said to answer that unasked question. "But we in motion. Never know what might happen."

So much was said in what went unsaid. She had to offer him some reassurance in reply to the shared knowledge that he was not cooperating.

"I hear you," Benzo said, confident in her.

"So, I might come check you out, but my schedule kind of tight," she said, wondering if it would have been better to say that she was also under investigation and visiting wouldn't help matters.

"I hear you."

"Cool," she said, ready to move on. She'd done her

part. "I'll get with Saul after the bail hearing," she added, wondering what it would take to get to five million dollars.

She could feel Benzo's understanding and hope as she dialed Mr. Toole's home number. He was never late. The man who answered the phone was not Mr. Toole. She hadn't expected Malik to answer the phone. He reminded her of Tootie Reese, her husband, and a hood legend.

Chapter Six

Basketball Dreams... Or Fast Money

The scene replayed itself over and over again. Giant gold eagles descended from a thunderous, darkened sky to hover above him, their large metallic wings making the sound of curving steel in the wind. When the eagles rose to the sky it opened up and rained down upon flaky white snow.

And repeat. Except this time the snow became slushy and warm, wetness and warmth concentrating at the bulbous *head of his dick.* The pulling, sucking, stroking sensation tugged him from a dream that left him both intrigued and confused.

"Baby," Malik groaned, reaching to her head.

"Mm… hmmm," moaned Trinity around his dick in her mouth.

Malik grunted, heaving his hips as she sucked the nectar from him, squeezing his balls all the while.

Malik exhaled mightily when she finally popped off his dick, smacked her lips, then laid the limp, spent meat to his thigh.

"You were having a bad dream," said Trinity. "It was time to get up anyway."

Malik leaned on one elbow, looking for his pager on the nightstand.

"It's just Shoota," said Trinity. "What happened on the 'Shaw last night?"

"Nothing much," replied Malik, studying his pager, but thinking of seeing Freeway Rick on Crenshaw. His respect in the streets represented money; a modern day Al Capone. Serving intoxicants during a time of prohibition. A new drug for the ghetto.

"I heard somebody got jacked at Shell."

"Everybody know Shell ain't the place to get gas." Trinity studied him, wondering why he was fake looking at his pager like he had a hundred messages.

"Can you see the two pages from Shoota?" she asked sweetly, mockingly.

The ringing phone saved him from sharing. He oddly felt a sense of pending change.

"Hello?"

"Uhm, excuse me. This is Roxanne calling for Mr. Toole."

Malik felt Trinity watching him from her position laying across his knees.

"Wassup, Roxanne," he replied, without emotion.

"Hi, Malik. Your grandfather hasn't shown up. Is he there? Or maybe at the doctor?"

Malik looked to Trinity. "G here?" he asked.

"He was leaving when I got up to pee."

"When was that?" Malik's body tightened.

"'Bout a hour ago. He was going to the gas station to get oil."

He relaxed, but hated that he forgot to put oil in the car. "He had to make a stop. He should be there in a few," he assured Roxanne.

"Oh. Ok. Thank you."

"What happened?" asked Trinity when the phone was returned to its cradle.

"G late for work."

"Him and your mom left together," added Trinity.

That explains everything, Malik thought to himself, relaxing on a pillow, crossing his fingers over his stomach and looking at the ceiling. *I gotta figure this shit out. Basketball camp might be cool. Get away for a minute.*

"Your mom was talking about how she hope you cut the grass," Trinity said. "I was walking up." She chuckled and added, "She looked surprised to see me. I thought she wasn't gonna say I could come in."

Malik looked down the length of his body at the top of her head. "Why you make it like she ain't tryna see you with me?" he asked.

"Don't play, Malik," she responded shortly, turning to look at him. "You know ain't nobody good enough for yo mama's son."

Malik silently agreed, yet neglected to remind her that she'd never been turned away. Losing this thread, he picked up another thought as he remained silent, staring blindly upwards.

"I was thinking about going to basketball camp," he said, not looking at her, but feeling her eyes on him.

"Ain't that what the coach at USC said you should do?"

Malik couldn't be sure by her tone if she was for or against camp.

"But he didn't say if I'm guaranteed a scholarship."

"You need a guarantee?" asked Trinity. "Sometimes people just want to see if you're willing to work for it."

This last statement cut Malik deep. He could hear himself defending his laziness. He couldn't be mad at her for being real with him.

"Twelve hundred dollars will get me to camp," whispered Malik, resolved to go. Now the question was how to get the money.

Trinity rubbed his stomach, dragging her pink nails across the muscled ridges.

"Shoota got some crack," said Malik casually. "He finna start selling."

Trinity chuckled, her chin resting on his thigh. "He ain't gone do nothing but go to jail," she giggled out.

"He spent a hundred dollars. He mighta made five hundred last night."

"But damn," began Trinity, "for every rock he sell that's a chance he gotta take. I could see if he was taking one chance for a lot of money."

Malik had to agree with her. He now saw the stupidity of what Shoota hoped to achieve while taking so many chances.

But all I need is twelve hundred, he thought to himself.

"What your grandfather say?" asked Trinity.

"He say if I get a job he'll loan me the money."

Trinity shrugged. "Well, get a job," she said.

"I won't be able to keep it 'cuz camp is for eight weeks. All day. Every day."

"Get a job at night then."

Malik had thought of this, but dismissed the option as a final, hopefully unnecessary option. He reached for the ringing phone, ignoring the simultaneous buzzing of his pager.

"Nigga, I sold that whole pack last night. Chopped them bitches in half and made damn near a million dollars," Shoota said in one excited breath, chuckling at his own exaggeration.

Malik saw that it was Shoota paging him at the same time, excited to share his crack selling triumph.

"That's cool," Malik responded coolly.

"What's up for the day?" asked Shoota. "I'm finna re-up."

"Nothing right now," responded Malik, thinking he would go get a newspaper. See who was hiring for night jobs.

"Ima come scoop you then."

Malik hesitated. He could feel Trinity listening. "Bring me a newspaper," he compromised.

Replacing the phone receiver, Malik looked to his girl. "He made a million dollars last night," he said.

Trinity remained silent. The phone rang, piercing the pregnant silence.

"Hello," Malik answered the phone.

The caller asked for his mother, then asked if he knew or was related to Marvellus Toole.

"Who is this?" Malik finally said, impatient and concerned by the official tone of the white lady.

"I apologize. My name is Tendra Rockingham with the Sheriff's office."

"What can I do for you?"

"I need to speak to a family member of Marvellus Toole, owner of a late model Lincoln Continental."

Malik's heart quickened. "I'm his grandson."

37

"I'm sorry to inform you that your grandfather has been in an automobile accident..."

Malik could only hear Lady Of Mercy Hospital after that. He thanked the police lady and hung up before she had a chance to say goodbye.

Trinity was already looking at him expectantly, her nickel-colored eyes blazing when he said, "G been in a accident."

Chapter Seven

Death Knockin' At The Door

The small waiting room of Lady Of Mercy Hospital was chaotic. Malik led his mother and Trinity through the front glass doors. Shoota was parking the Cutlass.

There was a stand in the middle of the waiting room between a set of Crips and equal number of Bloods. It was quickly apparent that both sets had a fellow wounded member there.

"Not in here! Not today," shouted a dark-skinned lady with blue eye shadow. She rose from her chair behind the glass partition to the far right of the room. L.A.P.D. officers strode in behind Trinity. They immediately fanned out before Malik, taking up too much space, encircling both sets of gang members. A baby cried without pause along one of the rows of seats, seated with both frightened and curious onlookers. The Crips were the first to blink, peeling from their position, probably because they were closest to the door.

The pigs watched silently, without question, as the blue khaki pants, white t-shirts and Chuck Taylor wearing Crips eased out the front door, their menacing eyes never leaving the Bloods.

Malik darted through a gap in the pigs' circle, stopping before the dark-skinned lady behind the glass partition.

"Hi, I'm looking for Marvellus Toole," announced Malik breathlessly.

"And who are you, sir?" responded the lady, her eyes taking in Malik's mother as she approached.

"I'm his daughter, Viva Toole. This is his grandson, Malik Toole."

Malik reached for Trinity and brought her close to him. The lady looked to a clipboard before her, scanning her bright purple fingernail down a list of names. At the bottom she popped her gum and reached for another clipboard.

"Lady Of Mercy, right?" asked Malik's mother, loud enough for the lady with the blue eye shadow to hear.

Bernetta, as her nametag implied, looked from the second clipboard obviously irritated. "Is there a page three for emergency intake?" she asked, turning to a chubby blonde woman behind the next window.

The blonde lady frowned. "Who are you looking for?" she asked, looking to Malik.

"Marvellus Toole," replied Bernetta.

The blonde lady lost her frown slowly then brightened. "Oh!" She jumped. "He was transferred to the V.A.," she added.

"Veteran Administration hospital," explained Bernetta, popping her gum again.

Malik's mother sighed. "That's way downtown," she complained, seeing the distance across the city from LaBrea to deep downtown. In a car without air conditioning on a hot day.

"What kind of person let an eight-year-old sit in their lap and drive in traffic?" said Malik's mother from the passenger seat of the Cutlass. She'd spoken to the white police lady, who explained that it was a child driver who caused the accident.

Shoota remained silent, having been put into cab duty. He'd planned on getting more rocks from Hill.

"White people," replied Trinity.

"And why they have to transfer him?" his mother went on, her silver bracelets jangling with a flick of her wrists. "That's more traveling. That's some bullshit. The V.A. ain't nobody."

Malik felt her anger. It only masked her fear. No one was willing to say that G was old. And slim. No one had been able to tell them the extent of his injuries, except that only the doctor could give out that information.

The Veteran Administration hospital resembled a welfare building. The people looked just as hopeful, yet disappointed there. And Shoota had to find and pay for parking, which he didn't like. Not the paying part, but the walking for many blocks on the streets of downtown.

Most of the people in the lobby were old and mostly black. They were the wives, mothers, and sisters of veterans. Perhaps a few daughters.

"Marvellus Toole, please," said Malik's mother, the first

to get to the plain white lady behind a high desk.

The dutiful office manager scanned a clipboard and looked up with an encouraging smile. "He's on the second floor. You can wait in Post Surgery," she offered, pointing to an elevator to her left.

Post Surgery was nothing more than a small room with two rows of chairs, most occupied by a huddling Asian family. There were only two open chairs. Trinity sat down to reserve them while Malik and his mother approached the weary-looking slender white man behind the opened half door.

Malik was the one to ask about his grandfather. The slender man assured them that the doctor would be out shortly.

"This is a sorry ass place," said Malik's mother, striding lazily to the chair beside Trinity.

Malik walked causally around the room, studying the many posters framed or taped to the avocado green walls. There was a poster over a sunrise in a wheat field. It read: To get well is to be well.

Every new poster with its supposedly inspirational words only provided a distraction. To think of being with G closed Malik's throat, threatening his breathing.

Malik had made a full loop around the room, stopping to drink out the water fountain between the bathroom doors at the back of the room, when he saw Roxanne step off the elevator across the narrow hallway. He caught her eyes as she looked into the room.

She was a peacock in knee high Gucci boots and caramel suede riding pants. Today, gold dolphin earrings bangle on her lobes, shimmering against the red tint of her feathered hair.

Malik started her way, meeting her near the reception desk. He felt Trinity's eyes on him from two rows away. Up on her now, he realized that the gold in her square Gucci frames was real.

"Hi, Malik. They called my office," said Roxanne, reaching out to touch his elbow.

"We waiting on the doctor," replied Malik.

"Doctor Gold?" she asked.

Malik just now realized he didn't know the doctor's name. Didn't think to ask. He stepped with Roxanne to the lady behind the counter.

"Hi. My name is Roxanne Reese for Doctor Gold." Her eyes followed as the lady's hand moved to the desk phone.

Malik grinned, impressed by the sound of the good doctor being paged to reception over the intercom.

"Do you know her?" asked Malik, nodding to the bullied white lady.

"Nope. But I'm sure she's nice though."

"So, they called you?" asked Malik, wanting to know why, but only because he was at a loss for words.

"Yes. I bring him here sometimes. They have me down as a contact."

Malik was not surprised. Almost thankful, except that he'd always thought of his grandfather as a healthy man. Roxanne was obviously closer than he figured. He now recognized why she'd always treated him as someone she knew intimately.

"Has anyone said how he's doing?" she asked.

"Naw. Just said to wait here."

Roxanne looked around the room for the first time. Seeing no open seats she sets her eyes back on Malik. "Have you given any more thought to basketball camp?"

"Actually, I have. G was gonna loan me the money if I got a job."

That option seemed to add to the uncertainty of the current situation. Basketball camp was yet still far

43

away. Malik felt no disappointment. Only concern for his grandfather.

"Look," began Roxanne, "come by the shop tomorrow. I might have some work for you."

Malik couldn't imagine what kind of work she could have for him. He briefly thought her selfish for trying to replace his grandfather right now, but the sincerity in her light brown eyes kept him from this. He got the feeling she'd long ago wanted to have a conversation with him.

A pale, slender white man burst through the white double doors, grabbing the attention of the entire room.

"Doctor Gold," whispered Roxanne, moving in his direction, motioning Malik to follow.

Trinity and Malik's mother joined the threesome just after Roxanne had introduced Malik, turning to his mother now, introducing her to the doctor. Roxanne's wrist sparkled with diamond tennis bracelets extending her hand to Trinity.

Malik accepted Trinity in his embrace as they all turned to the bleary eyed doctor, his blue eyes already showing remorse.

Malik's mother was the first to cry out, her arms falling around her waist. He held Trinity while moving towards his mother, whose wails screamed into his shoulder. The doctor droned on about Marvellus's internal injuries being too severe.

Malik was numb, barely hearing his mother's cry, or feeling Roxanne gently rubbing his shoulder.

Chapter Eight

Comfort Me

The cronic smoke felt good coursing through Malik's lungs. The darkened sky hid the look of loss in his eyes. Funny how one minute they were there and the next minute they were gone.

"Thas crazy, man," Shoota said from the chair next to Malik, for the third time out of nowhere, his thoughts coming out in those three words.

Malik handed Shoota the joint, the smell of chicken coming through the screen door, reminding him he had eaten nothing all day.

"What else yo' mom cooking?" asked Malik.

"Shit, she teaching my lil' sister how to cook," responded Shoota, trying to keep the cronic smoke in his lungs.

Malik looked to the dooky brown Cadillac Brougham gliding by, the gold flake making the brown sparkle. There were three heads in the car. Dutch was driving.

Malik wondered if Dutch really offered to sell double-up to Shoota. He watched the tail lights until Dutch turned in his yard.

"So, she say to come through, huh?" said Shoota, passing the joint to Malik. "She prolly want you to take his place, but what about his other spots?"

Malik looked to Shoota. "What you mean?"

"Don't he be cleaning up at a few spots?" Shoota said. "I thought he had like a lil' cleaning business. That's why I thought you wasn't trippin' about b-ball camp. Figured you was cool with working with G."

Malik grinned, remembering when G did have a few buildings under contract with about four or five workers. Then one of his workers started stealing. Anything. People's account numbers. Company clothes. Office phones, pagers, and leftover wine from an office party. His business was doomed when a surveillance video surfaced featuring two of his workers having sex on a manager's desk at his biggest office building.

"Naw. Not no more," replied Malik.

"Thas crazy," repeated Shoota. Malik silently agreed.

Shoota was the first to see the black Cadillac, its tail jacked in the air. It wasn't hard to tell that the two light-skinned men inside were dangerous. Hill and his brother, Al.

"There dem niggas right there." Shoota hit the joint one more time before handing it off to Malik.

Malik inhaled slowly, watching Shoota walk with wide steps to the curb, his pants hanging low around his upper thighs. He was holding them up by the belt, his blue checkered boxers hugging his ass cheeks.

The exchange was quick. Shoota skipped back up the walkway clutching a brown paper bag. He took his seat again before pulling out a sandwich bag of white rocks. He rolled the bag in his palm, feeling its worth.

"Ima break all these down and get about two thousand dollars," said Shoota, holding the bag of rocks out to Malik.

"That's a lot of people you gotta sell to," said Malik, not impressed by the many chances to go to jail.

"Naw," answered Shoota, bringing the bag back. "Everybody want this shit. This cavi right here. Look." He pointed across the street where a heavy man was watering his grass and smoking a cigarette.

"Mister Foster?" asked Malik, thinking of the man's wife and two small twin girls. He worked at Pep Boys as a mechanic.

"Watch this," invited Shoota, standing to call Mr. Foster from across the street.

The portly, short man with a small afro looked both ways before crossing the street, the water hose left to soak the center of his lawn.

"Wassup old man," said Shoota smiling when Mr. Foster reached the bottom of the porch.

"Hi y'all doing?" responded Mr. Foster, avoiding eye contact with Malik, not sure if he should protest what business he anticipated Shoota was about to share openly.

Shoota had split a dime-sized crack rock with his fingernail. He handed the smaller piece to Mr. Foster's outstretched palm. "Test that for me," instructed Shoota.

Malik watched as the dark man's large eyes looked around nervously.

"Go ahead," urged Shoota. "Ain't nobody looking."

Mr. Foster crouched to the porch, beside a bush. He

pulled a glass pipe from the front pocket of his jeans and placed the small rock in its bowl. The flame was bright, making the rock sizzle when Mr. Foster inhaled the acrid smoke. He pinched his nose, his eyes shutting tight. When he exhaled and opened his eyes they were bloodshot red. He nodded. Smacked his lips. Shuffled his feet.

"That's cavi, ain't it?" asked Shoota, smiling proudly.

Mr. Foster nodded, losing what esteem he had as a hard-working family man right before Malik's eyes.

"Bring me some customers," said Shoota, shooing Mr. Foster away.

"That's crazy," offered Malik, shaking his head in dismay.

"That ain't shit," said Shoota. "You know fine ass Lola, from next door?"

Malik nodded, the secretive look in Shoota's eyes signaling this was going to be good.

Lola was the prettiest lady on the block. Studying to be a nurse. Her mother passed away and left the house to her.

"She smoke primos," announced Shoota.

Malik didn't pretend to know what that meant.

"She crumble a piece of crack in with her weed and smoke it like that," he explained. "Won't be long before she on the pipe though. Ima be right here waiting."

Malik looked out to the street, never imagining that Lola even smoked weed. He watched as Mr. Foster moved with a new energy as he coiled the water hose against the side of his house.

"Tootie Reese got a son by her. He got her that shop," said Shoota, bouncing the baggy of rocks in his palm.

"Who?"

"Roxanne," replied Shoota. "I recognized who she was when I saw her Maxima at the hospital.

"Who is Tootie Reese?" Malik wanted to know.

"He from Shotgun. He put that whole hood on. That nigga on death row though." Malik absorbed this information, making her interest in him more meaningful.

"She put that nigga Benzo Al on, but the feds just snatched that nigga up," added Shoota.

Malik couldn't be sure if this bit of information was offered as hood gossip or as a warning. He rose to go, feeling a sudden heaviness and sense of loss.

"You don't want no chicken?" asked Shoota.

Malik inhaled deeply. "Naw. I'm cool," he replied, looking forward to the slow walk down the street to his house.

"Want me to take you to her shop tomorrow?"

"Yeh. I gotta pick up his stuff."

Shoota rose, following Malik to the edge of the lawn. "I wonder what else she want?"

Malik didn't respond. He felt selfish when it came to Roxanne. He'd rather Shoota not take him. He was thankful that Shoota stayed behind as he walked away. He didn't want to talk about his drug selling or about Roxanne. Slow tears drop from Malik's eyes during his leisurely walk down the darkened street. He realized that his grandfather would not be sitting in his usual spot in the living room, cracking open roasted peanuts. He regretted anew that he had failed to put oil in the car like he'd asked.

The smell of baked apples greeted Malik when he entered his house. He could see his mother moving around in the kitchen at the other end of the living room. A quick peek into his bedroom on the way to the kitchen revealed the raised, rounded butt of Trinity laying in his bed.

He was able to watch his mother for a second before she realized he was standing at the door. She carefully placed the hot apple pie on the stove before walking over to him. Wrapping her arms around his waist, she looks into his grief-stricken eyes.

"I'm so sorry," she said.

Malik returned her hug, the words meaning nothing. "Yeh. Me too," he replied before loosening his embrace and turning for his room.

"Want a piece of apple pie?" she asked softly.

"Maybe later, Mom."

Malik closed the door behind him, expecting Trinity to stir on the bed. She remained motionless. He leaned over her, brushing soft strands of hair away from her sleeping face.

He stood, admiring her sleeping form. Her petite curvy body caught his breath. He was reminded of the first time he saw her. She was practicing cheerleading drills in the gym before basketball practice. She'd seemed to be cheering especially for him.

He was instantly hard, his jeans holding his erection down like a wrestler. He shed them, his erect dick springing through the opening in his boxers. He leaned low, pushing her loose shorts to the side.

When the head of his swollen dick met her pussy she moaned. He moved the head in a slow circle, waking up her desire. She grew moist, allowing the head to nudge its way through her lips.

She lifted her hips slightly as he pulled off her shorts. Her lace panties slid to the side easily as he pushed into her slowly, her wetness allowing more of him inside her with each slow stroke. He grunted with pleasure when he filled her up to the hilt, feeling her body shift and adjust to his entry.

"Uhhmm," she moaned under him, moving her hips up.

Malik went in and out. Slow at first. Then faster, losing himself in her, blinded to her growing whispers.

"Malik. Baby."

This encouraged him, ignoring her attempt to brace

her hand to his chest. He chased her movements, blinded to her pain and subtle escape. Malik was driving into her madly, his pain streaming through his body, meeting red hot at the head of his dick. Her cries weren't heard until he'd spent himself inside of her.

His tender apologies brushed hot against her neck as she lay collapsed beneath him. He rolled away from her, thankful for her forgiveness as she turned to embrace him, offering the comfort he needed.

Chapter Nine

The Drop Off

Mario's Auto Repair sat in the middle of Vernon Avenue between San Pedro and Main Street on the East Side. The small entrance was nearly hidden from view because it sat back from the sidewalk. It was the oily sign above and black grill gate that served as landmarks. Across the street was a tire shop that specialized in buying old tires and selling retreads.

Roxanne's gleaming gold-flaked, magenta-colored Maxima looked out of place amidst the older model cars squeezed into Mario's small repair yard. Two familiar men were stationed under a raised Camaro in the garage. To the left, a trio of Chevy Novas sat stationed like soldiers prepared for instructions. Roxanne wondered which one, if not all, concealed cocaine.

Mario appeared from the edge of the garage, standing at its oily mouth looking into the yard, exploding into a wide smile at the sight of Roxanne. It was the biggest thing on his slim frame, his pants and blue khaki shirt hanging loosely from his narrow shoulders.

"*Hola, mi amiga,*" he called out, wiping his hands on a dingy red rag.

"Hi, Mario. How are you?" replied Roxanne, remaining in her car in case she might be asked to move it to the side.

Mario came to a leisurely stop at her door, his top lip hidden by a massive mustache. Bushy eyebrows and an unruly mop of hair gave him the look of a mad scientist.

"Business looks good, Mario," said Roxanne, stalling her unfortunate news.

Mario looked back to the garage as if seeing it through her eyes. He nodded. "It is okay," he agreed in his clipped English. "How are things for you?"

She exhaled, shaking her head. "Not good, Mario," she said, looking into his dark eyes. "Feds got my guy," she said.

Mario looked to the street casually, across to the tire shop while stroking one end of his mustache. "Is not good," he said finally, adding, "must be careful."

"Yes. I know. My guy is solid. I have to bail him out ASAP."

"How much?"

Roxanne hated to say that his bail was five million dollars, but she did, not surprised that Mario let out an incredulous whistle.

"Is too much," said Mario. "Is a lot too much money."

"Yes. I know," she agreed.

53

"Maybe you cancel order?"

Roxanne had gone to ask him for an extension on what she owed. Benzo was arrested with twenty kilos of cocaine in his truck. Today was supposed to be the day to pay for it.

"Do I have to?" she asked.

Mario waved this off. "Too much cocaine," he said with a smile. "You okay."

Roxanne was glad to hear this. She imagined that Mario had access to more cocaine than he could sell. She also imagined that it cost him a fraction of the five thousand per kilo that he charged her. With kilos going for fifteen to twenty on the street, the loss had already been paid for with previous profits. If not for outstanding legal bills and the cost of living, Roxanne would be in good shape, but she realized she needed a good summer to get back right.

"So, what you got for me, Mario?" she asked, prepared to sell dope herself if she had to, no matter the risk.

Mario gestured towards the Chevy Novas behind him. "Ten, twenty, thirty," he shrugged, turning back to her. "One hundred kilos. No matter," he said casually.

One hundred kilos, she said to herself. Not since Tootie was home had she seen one hundred kilos. With his arrest, most of his buyers went elsewhere. She suspected Freeway Rick took up the slack. Her body shivered at the thought of pushing one hundred kilos a week. But for now ten would have to do.

"It'll have to be ten," she said.

Mario held up two fingers. "Two times. One hundred. Next week, no?"

Roxanne nodded with understanding. She owed fifty thousand for half of the last twenty and fifty for the next one. Her body tingled with what she hoped wais just adrenaline, and not fear of what could happen if this shipment went bad.

"Yes," she said. "Give me a week."

"You take today?"

"In the morning," she replied, already lining up the phone calls she had to make to her buyers.

"*Bueno*," said Mario, nodding. "Is good for you my friend."

His smile reassured Roxanne, but she reminded herself that his smile could just as easily turn to a wicked frown. She didn't want to see his frown, more importantly, she didn't want to disappoint him in the name of her husband.

The still rising sun shimmered on to the morning street, offering a glowing backdrop to the live city of Los Angeles. Girls in biker shorts and wearing dookie braids provided eye candy for passersby. Roxanne didn't realize she hadn't eaten until she neared Figueroa. Tam's Burgers, a popular eatery, made the corner of Vernon and Figueroa pop with delicious food. It also served as a post up spot for tow trucks waiting for their next call.

Roxanne pulled into Tam's parking lot, stopping next to a gold candy painted Cadillac Brougham with a chandelier inside. The small tires gleamed with Armour All, wrapping gold Dayton rims.

She knew the driver. She could see him, with two similarly dressed men, standing at a Pac-Man game near the Tam's order counter. Cookie, dressed in simple tan khaki pants and a white t-shirt, downplayed the rich status the new dope game had rewarded him with.

"Wassup, Roxy," said Cookie, peeling away from the men playing Pac-Man.

"Hey, Cookie," replied Roxanne, stepping to the large, midnight-colored man behind the order counter.

"You still getting money?" he asked while she look at the overhead menu.

"Not like you," she responded, ready to order a double cheeseburger, onion rings, and strawberry soda. She gave this order to the man everyone referred to as Tam. He'd never denied this to be his name.

"Too bad what happened to Benzo," said Cookie. "What they doing with him?"

Roxanne knew this would come. The streets wanted to know if he was cooperating or not. Will his arrest threaten their livelihood. Roxanne realized it was important to be seen unafraid.

"Got his bail sky high," she said, proud to be able to say it, though it made it tougher for her to get him out.

Cookie nodded, satisfied. "Benzo my boy," said Cookie, his jheri curl framing his dark face like an angelic halo.

"Mine too," responded Roxanne, watching her beef sizzle on the grill.

"On the real though, I miss Tootie. He showed me love." Cookie watched for her reaction.

Roxanne had always wondered where Cookie had gotten his dope. She wondered where he got it now and how much weight he was moving. She looked at him anew.

"So, what's up Cookie. I'm trying to get my husband off death row," she said. "You got room for me?"

Cookie grinned. "What you charging for a brick? I got 'em for seven five from hubby."

Roxanne didn't doubt this. She doubted he was getting a better price now.

"I wish I woulda knew you was holding it down for him," added Cookie.

Roxanne accepted this subtle lie. Cookie, like most of them, broke all ties with Tootie in the wake of his arrest. Anyone close to Tootie was put under a microscope.

"Well," began Roxanne, "checking ain't cheating."

"You right about that," responded Cookie.

"What you looking for?" she wanted to know, turning to him fully, prepared to do business.

"Straight up," said Cookie seriously. "I get fifty chickens at eight each." He said this as if he was upset at the price.

Roxanne frowned to accentuate the absurdity of it. She wanted to ask who he was paying that to, sure that it was a go-between, but didn't. She was also interested to know where his market was, surprised that he was pushing fifty birds at a time.

"I can get you fifty at seven," she said, happy to take a two thousand dollar profit for each kilo.

Cookie looked impressed. "Oh, so you do have Tootie's connect."

Cookie was called for his order. Tam pushed out several greasy bags to one of the men Cookie had instructed to get the food.

"You never asked, Cookie," said Roxanne, eager to get his business. "When you want that fifty?"

"I tell you what," he began, stepping closer. "If you can get me twenty at seven by this weekend I'll fuck with you."

"I'll have it for you tomorrow," she assured him with a wink and a satisfied grin.

Leaving Tam's for her salon, Roxanne thought about approaching the city's reputable to win their business. There were only a few who bought weight, but they could be the difference between living drop to drop and really stacking some serious bread for life's extravagances, legal bills, and surprise expenses.

Shoota's Cutlass was parked in her favored spot by the front door when she reached her salon. Malik got out the passenger side as she parked on the other side of the front door.

"Hi, Malik," she said, disguising her irritation as Shoota looked at her with hungry eyes. "I'm running late."

"It's cool. We just got here," offered Malik, taking her bag of food as she opened the front door.

"Your grandfather is usually here first," she said, leading the way inside, cutting on the lights.

Malik felt his grandfather's presence in the quiet salon. He could see him moving around fixing things and making sure Roxanne was okay. He was contemplating what he would say if she asked him to take his grandfather's place when she called for him to follow her to the office.

Malik sat in the chair in front of her desk, wondering when did the salon get crowded. Above her was a framed picture of her in a fur coat standing next to a tall, light-skinned man in a silk suit and big gold ropes around his neck. Behind them was a white Rolls Royce.

"So, how are you?" she asked, wasting no time pulling her burger and onion rings from the greasy bag.

"I'm good. Just getting used to G not being at home."

Roxanne nodded, slicing her burger in half. She slid half across to Malik. When he started to decline she said, "This is called breaking bread together. You don't wanna eat with me?" she asked pointedly.

Malik submitted, accepting half her onion rings and strawberry soda she poured into a cup for him.

"Who's your friend?" she asked, taking a bite of her burger.

"Shoota. We go way back," Malik said, feeling himself defend Shoota, but understanding her suspicion. She was right to be suspicious of Shoota.

"Your grandfather didn't describe you as someone who needs company."

Malik felt good knowing that his grandfather talked about him.

"He was so proud of you," she added. "He would tell me about all your games. I feel like I've seen you play myself." She giggled with this.

Malik liked her immediately. He'd always thought she

was stuck up. He saw now why his grandfather was so loyal to her.

"I asked you to come so I could give your grandfather's things to you," she said, looking across the desk at Malik.

Malik was waiting for her to produce his stuff, but instead, she fixed him with a hard stare.

"But I have another idea," she began, "I believe we can help each other."

Malik still hadn't decided if he wanted to work in a hair salon when she asked if he did drugs.

"No," he replied, wondering why this mattered.

"Ever sell drugs?" she asked.

"Nope," he said, thinking of Shoota.

"What do you think of drug dealers?"

Malik shrugged, remembering Shoota told him about her husband and Benzo Al. "They okay with me," he said casually.

Roxanne studied Malik for a beat before she asked, "Would you be interested in making some extra money?"

Malik looked skeptical, still doubtful he'd say yes to working in her salon. "Doing what?" he asked.

"I've got a few packages I need dropped off."

Malik's heart thumped hard. Shoota was right. He'd suggested she might ask him to deliver dope for her on the drive there. He'd laughed it off, unwilling to consider the possibility.

"Did I say something wrong? Did I offend you?"

"Naw... Naw. It's cool," replied Malik, shaking off his new realized perception of her. "What you need dropped off?"

"Cocaine," she answered simply. "I'll give you a car and pay you a thousand dollars for each delivery."

Malik had mixed emotions. Drugs. Basketball camp.

"It's easy," added Roxanne. "These are my people. No

drama. Drop it off and get the money. Simple."

Simple, he repeated to himself, thinking with a couple drops he could go to basketball camp. He was nodding his agreement before he realized his head was moving. He liked the happy look on her face.

Chapter Ten

Keep Your Eye On The Prize

"So how much you gotta drop off?" Trinity wanted to know, looking to Malik as he hung up the phone.

Malik remained seated at the desk while Trinity lay on his bed, on one elbow, her head resting on her palm. "She didn't say," he replied, fingering the coiled telephone cord.

"I knew she wanted you for something."

"Her last drop off guy got arrested," offered Malik, immediately regretting it.

Trinity sat up on the bed. "What?! And here you come. What if you get arrested?"

"You the one said Shoota was stupid for taking chances for change."

"But you don't even know how much you gon' be having or for how long."

"It's only for a coupla times 'til I get enough for camp."

Trinity seemed calmed by this. "So, she know Shoota taking you to get it and stuff?"

Malik shrugged. "He was there already," he responded.

"That's different than him going with you on your drops," she pointed out.

"Is he getting paid too?"

"Stop asking me all these questions," he complained.

"Somebody need to ask you 'cuz you acting stupid right now. If it was me I wouldn't let Shoota be all up in my business. And she prolly feel that way too."

Malik remained silent. He'd never considered separating Shoota from what he had going on with Roxanne.

"Well, it's your life. I hope you know what you're doing," Trinity said into the silence. Malik joined her on the bed and wrapped her in his arms. She playfully resisted at first. He told her that he loved her. She said it back.

"This is for both of us," he said low. "Me and you."

"Just be careful," she whispered back, a lone tear dropping from her eye.

Malik was kissing her imaginary tears away when Shoota pulled up outside and bumped his horn. "Be back in a few," he said, softly struggling to free himself from her grasp.

"Noooooo," she playfully cried out, reaching for him as he moved towards the bedroom door.

What Trinity said about including Shoota in his business woke him up to how much he should share and keeping future business to himself.

"You good?" asked Malik from the passenger seat of the Cutlass, noting his odd quietness.

"Yeh. I'm straight my nigga," replied Shoota, turning off the block. "I was just thinking..."

"What about?" asked Malik, not sure he wanted to know. Only yesterday Shoota had a grand idea to keep track of all the people who Roxanne sold dope to so they could go back and rob them. Malik had to remind him that this was temporary, which only made Shoota feel more right about his plan.

"I was thinking," began Shoota, "we get us a dope spot together. See, I was already gonna do it, but together we can sell halves and wholes out that bitch." He looked to Malik. "What... you ain't feeling that?"

"I'm going to play basketball, man," Malik reminded him.

They almost passed up Mario's Auto Repair. Traffic was light because it was nearly closing time. Mario greeted Malik and gave him the keys to a yellow Chevy Nova. Malik immediately liked the feel of the car and wondered if this was the one she was giving him to drive.

Malik led the way to a house on 65th and Normandie, not far from where he lived on 41st and Figueroa. He never would've suspected that on this quiet street major drug transactions were being made.

The porch light was on at the small white house, its blue trim bright in the growing darkness. Roxanne's Maxima was parked at the back of the driveway. Malik pulled in behind her. Shoota parked at the curb.

Roxanne surprised Malik when she stepped out the back door as he was getting out the car. She was hidden in the shadows, standing at the corner of the house.

"Go send your friend home," she said, her voice laced

with frustration. Malik didn't question her. There was no need for Shoota to stay anyway. He met Shoota halfway up the driveway.

"I'm straight homie," said Malik, walking back towards the street so that Shoota would follow.

"She here?" asked Shoota. "Bitch told you I can't stay, huh?"

"Naw. It ain't like that. She just got people coming through and we gonna be outta here in a minute anyway," offered Malik, feeling exposed and out of place talking to Shoota in front of a drug house. Shoota absorbed this rejection, looking back to the house as he was considering confronting Roxanne.

"I'll be straight. Don't trip," said Malik. "I'll hit you up later."

"Aiight," Shoota said, giving up his anger. "I got some shit to handle anyway." Malik turned to walk back up the driveway when Shoota called him back.

"Don't let that bitch play you. That's why she don't want me here cuz she know you my boy and ain't gon' let you get played," Shoota whispered this with conviction, waiting for Malik to nod his agreement, giving him dap.

Roxanne was waiting for Malik when he reached the backyard. "I know y'all boys, but my business is with you," she said from the shadows. "The less he know about my business the better. You need to adopt that rule."

Malik remembered Trinity saying the same thing.

"Okay," breathed out Roxanne. "Let's unload this stuff."

Malik opened the trunk and took out the spare tire. Lifting the panel he discovered thirty kilos of cocaine. He took a deep breath to remain cool.

"You ever see this much dope before?" she asked, standing next to him.

Malik shook his head, eyeing the embossed red rooster

on each brick of powder cocaine.

"We've got a few people coming through to buy this tonight. I'm going to introduce you so you can deliver to them personally next time. In the next few days I'm going to send you out of town."

This is real, he thought to himself as he grabbed up a few bricks to put in a large duffel bag Roxanne was holding. *Just 'til I get enough for basketball camp,* he reminded himself without much conviction.

Chapter Eleven

The Referral

Saul had the look of a man with a devilish secret. He set the thick envelope stuffed with money on his desk, leaning back in his fat leather chair.

"So, you plucking off the Tootie Reese tree, huh?" he asked, forcing his stubby arms behind his head. His expensive suit fit him as if needing more fabric.

"Well." Roxanne sighed. "Might as well put ten toes down."

Saul nodded, grinning with pasty teeth. "Well, can't say that I'm mad at you," he responded, casting an appreciative look at the envelope of money. "This will go a long way to addressing your husband's cause."

Roxanne was not very confident that Tootie would be released from death row, considering he'd been offered up as the poster child of the new Los Angeles cocaine trade and a danger to law enforcement.

"Might take more than ten toes down to touch Benzo's bail, right?" asked Saul.

"Well, I have some new help," offered Roxanne. "Twenty toes down." She grinned with this, her brown eyes sparkling like her diamonds.

"Oy!" exclaimed Saul, leaning forward. "New guy?"

"Well, I'm grooming him. He's special though, I will say that."

Saul exhaled with concern. "Roxy," he began, "I care for you. You're a class act and we've always been straight with each other."

"Say it," urged Roxanne.

"You've got eyes on you. Benzo's arrest was no mistake."

"I know where those eyes are, Saul," Roxanne replied shortly, thinking of Hill. "I got it under control."

Saul was not convinced, shaking his head in dismay. "And now you got a new guy," he said. "I just hope he lasts until you get where you need to be."

"Why wouldn't he last, Saul? Please share more," responded Roxanne, trying to control her anger, eyeing the shifty man seriously.

"Look," began Saul, pressing his palms together before spreading them wide. "Let me help you. I've got an associate who may be interested in doing business with you."

"You in the drug business now, Saul?"

He grinned crookedly. "I know a guy," he offered, his grin spreading wider. "Joseph Mordecai. He's a club owner."

Roxanne remained calm, though silently excited at

what this could mean. "So, how long have you known this guy?" she asked, flipping the simple white business card Saul had passed to her between her fingers.

"By association we are old friends," he said mysteriously.

Roxanne was tempted to mistrust Saul, but her caution was softened when her lawyer mentions that this old friend by association was looking to move one hundred pounds of cocaine per week.

Saul nodded at Roxanne's surprised expression. "He's an international club promoter. He has the clientele, but not a reliable supply."

Now Roxanne understood. "What's your involvement?" she asked.

Saul shrugged. "Referral is my business. You win, I win."

From both ends, she thought to herself.

"He's prepared when you are," began Saul, "how about you have your new guy meet with him. I can say positively that he's prepared to purchase forty pounds as a show of good faith."

Roxanne silently did the math. Forty pounds was just over twenty kilos. "Would it be too much for him to deal in kilo units?" she asked lightly.

Saul nodded, understanding her point. "I'll let you handle that. And you can quote your own prices. I won't presume to know what's best." He showed that crooked grin again, satisfied with himself.

Roxanne had wondered what price this new client would expect and if Saul would have been so bold as to insinuate his estimated prices. She was still feeling a tingle of excitement when she left Saul's office. She would never have imagined that the demure lawyer would prove such utility.

Early afternoon traffic was light as she drove with new excitement on her way to Mario's Auto Repair. The ringing car phone interrupted her thoughts about what it would mean to push one hundred kilos per week.

"Hey, Roxy. Tell me something good homegirl," the familiar voice, feminine with masculine direction.

"Hey, Pearl," responded Roxanne.

"You ready to feed my dogs. They getting skinny on a bitch."

"Yep. I'll send somebody up there within the next couple of days," assured Roxanne.

"Oh, so Benzo ain't coming through?" said Pearl. "I love me some pussy, but I'm laying down for his fine ass." She giggled with this.

"No, not this time," replied Roxanne, avoiding saying more to avoid a lie.

"So, he ain't get locked up?"

Shit. Roxanne exhaled. "Yeh, girl. I'm getting him out soon though," assured Roxanne.

"Oh. Ok." Pearl paused before she said, "Everything good though?"

"Of course. As long as I'm here it's all good."

"That's what I'm talking about," replied Pearl, relieved. "I don't know why you scared to come up this way. I won't kidnap you and do crazy things to make you fall in love with me," joked Pearl.

"Girl, ain't nobody scared of you."

"Well, I dare you. LL Cool J got a concert up here. I got good seats. You should come."

"I don't do rap concerts. Not since niggas shot up the RUN DMC concert," said Roxanne. "But look, I'm pulling up to my appointment. I got you covered. Don't worry."

Roxanne was only two blocks away from Mario's shop when she ended the call. Her pager buzzed on the passenger seat. She smiled at the familiar number.

Her heart quickened at the sound of his voice when he answered. Michael Concepcion was her high school sweetheart. They would have married if he'd not been arrested for murder at sixteen and sent to jail until he was twenty-one.

"When you coming to see me," he said to her, simply, as he always did.

"Soon," she replied, reluctant to meet him in Watts. Word would surely get back to Tootie.

"What I gotta do, make it 'bout business?"

"Of course not. What are you talking about?"

"I hear good thangs 'bout that hard. I'm tryna see what a brick of powder do for me?"

Roxanne grinned. Michael Concepcion ran Watts. His wealth and hood loyalty came from his PCP drug sales. To hear that he wanted to get into the cocaine business was a welcomed announcement.

"Well, we can definitely discuss it," she assured him, pulling into Mario's Auto Repair where she found Mario talking to a tall black man, apparently about his Trans Am.

"That's what I wanna hear. Let's make it before the weekend. I'm heading to San Berdu to check out that Cool J concert."

"Oh, really," replied Roxanne, for a moment feeling as if she was missing out on something.

"Yeh. You know my boy Kool Moe Dee though. He might show up. They got a lil' beef going."

"That's what got the RUN concert shot up. I'll pass." She waved to Mario, who accepted a wrinkled wad of money from the tall man. "But we'll definitely get together before the weekend," she assured him.

Mario began walking her way as she ended her call. When he leaned to her window she handed him two

McDonald's food bags. They were stocked with counted bands of money.

"I'll need fifty for the weekend," she announced.

Mario smiled. "This is good, no?"

"Yes." She smiled back. "This is good. The same guy will be by before you close. Yes?"

"Of course. I have red car ready," he said, making a grand sweep to a row of cars behind him.

Not bad start to the day, she whispered to herself as she left Mario's Auto Repair, before remembering that the funeral for Marvellus Toole was about to be underway. She spied a flower shop to stop at before she headed to pay her respects to the man she'd grown to love as a father.

Chapter Twelve

Saying Goodbye

Inglewood Cemetery looked like the front of a church from Florence Avenue, once you made that right on Centinela, all of its haunting green quiet was visible. Granite headstones rose from the rolling lanes of grass like sentries at the door to the next life.

Amidst this quiet greenery, before a newly engraved headstone, stood Malik with his mother. With them were the old withered friends of his grandfather. More were dead than alive, buried along these grassy lanes.

"...and Lord we ask that you accept this new soldier

into your bosom," the sharply dressed preacher said, holding his shiny Bible close to his broad chest.

Malik stared at the gleaming, gold-finished coffin, a product of Malik's first night of work with Roxanne. His mother hadn't questioned where he'd gotten the money, nor had she questioned him when he'd stocked the refrigerator with groceries.

"...he was a good man... an honest and hard-working man," the preacher continued.

The preacher's words of heavenly promise swam with Malik's thoughts of the glamor, riches, and possibilities of his immediate life. The sound and image of Cookie's money being shuffled by the money counter had hypnotized him.

Malik stood anew at the gates of death, wanting to live a life of thrilling reward. He thought how sad for his grandfather to have died nearly penniless after a life of military service and dashed dreams. Malik resolved that this would not be his end.

"...we beseech you, oh dear Lord, accept Marvellus Toole into your heavenly garden to rest at your golden feet," the preacher said, his tightly closed eyes facing skyward.

Shoota sucked his teeth next to Malik. He'd already shared with Malik his allergy to cemeteries. He'd promised to come only because it was G. Malik looked over to him, not surprised that a rash had not yet developed on his face.

Malik turned back to the preacher, coming to the end of his burial sermon, thinking of Shoota's new dress code. He no longer wore mostly khakis and t-shirts. He'd graduated to corduroys and polo shirts. His ever-present scheming grin was now less pronounced, but more deadly.

It was when Shoota sucked his teeth for the second time and Malik was ready to give him a hard stare, that he saw Roxanne standing at the edge of the massed funeral assembly.

Malik stood silently as his grandfather was lowered into the freshly dug earth. His mother stepped forward, her feet faltering. Malik assisted her as they approached the grave.

Malik held back tears as he let the first pile of dirt slide from the shovel on to the flower-covered casket. He absorbed his mother's weight as she struggled to maintain her composure.

With his grandfather in the ground and Trinity and his grief-stricken mother waiting for him in the once cocaine-laden, still borrowed Chevy Nova, Malik met with Roxanne. He felt Shoota, who was waiting for him, watching with calculating eyes.

"Is your mom okay?" asked Roxanne, looking like a hood princess in designer gear from her Louis Vuitton boots to her large gold-framed Louis Vuitton eyewear.

"Yeh, she'll be okay."

"And how are you?"

"I'm cool," responded Malik, having a sudden thought. "Who you gon' get to fix stuff at your salon?"

Roxanne hadn't considered this. "I'll have to find someone soon. The air conditioner ain't working."

"I thought when you said you wanted to talk to me that you were going to ask me to help out." He grinned with this.

"I did, didn't I? And how do you like it?" asked Roxanne, not daring to ask if he had enough for basketball camp, but sure that he did.

"It's cool," he replied, enjoying the use of the car and having money to help out around the house. "Let me ask you a question."

"Sure," responded Roxanne, stopping at her car door, noting Trinity watching them from across the parking lot.

"How much do you charge for one kilo?"

Roxanne was not surprised by his question. "It depends. It could cost twenty thousand depending on where and who you selling it to," she answered. "You got somebody wanna buy one?"

Malik regretted asking now, but he'd promised Shoota he would. "Yeh," he replied.

Roxanne decided not to press him, but offered him advice instead. "Be careful who you sell to and as a favor to whom."

Malik suspected she knew it was for Shoota.

"I've got the blueprint for you, Malik," said Roxanne. "Stay loyal and I'll make you rich. Doing favors for people will get you locked up."

"I gotta look out for Shoota," admitted Malik.

Roxanne nodded, understanding his situation. "Give him a ten thousand dollar price. He can get fifteen for it easy in the city, but knowing him he probably wants to open a crack house." She chuckled with this.

Malik grinned, remembering that Shoota did say that. "Cool," he replied, not telling her that Shoota wanted to sell a kilo to a Crip from Hoover named Shadow.

"So, we have a shipment ready. I won't be at the house," Roxanne informed him. "Can I trust you to get the product and take it to the house?"

"Yeh, I can handle it."

"Without Shoota, right?"

"Right," he assured her, understanding her reasons for keeping their business private.

With the business logistics handled Malik bid Roxanne farewell, never questioning why she would not be at the stash house later. Shoota was waiting for him before he could reach Trinity, who was standing at the door of the borrowed Chevy Nova, watching him.

"What she say?" asked Shoota.

"She'll give me one for ten," replied Malik, leaving the rest to himself.

Shoota frowned. "Ten?"

Malik nodded. "They go for fifteen right now."

"But this me! I know she can give it to me for cheaper than that," complained Shoota. Malik shrugged, ready to walk off.

"Aiiight," began Shoota, "when can I get the coke?"

"Whenever we get the money."

Shoota stared to the ground in thought, pinching his lips. "Okay. Cool. We gotta go see Shadow. When you gonna have it?"

"Tonight," answered Malik, immediately wishing he'd kept that to himself.

Shoota nodded excitedly. "That's cool. You rollin' with me or you wanna just give it to me?"

"I might not have time, but check with me later. I'm finna take moms home and chill."

Shoota accepted this, nodding with a crooked grin. "I'ma set it up then," he said.

Malik gave him dap before joining Trinity at the car. She was watching him closely. His mother was in the car, staring ahead, reminding Malik of her extreme grief. The drive home was sober and quiet save for Malik asking his mother if she was okay. She'd simply nodded. It wasn't until they get home that Trinity cornered Malik in his room.

"What you and that bitch got going on?" she asked, standing over him as he sat on the bed.

"Roxanne?"

Trinity rolled her eyes. "No! The fucking queen of England."

Malik placed his hands on her hips. "She just came to the funeral. You know G worked for her for a minute."

"And now you working for her." She pouted as Malik raised her dress, crawling the fabric up her thighs.

"You better be careful," warned Trinity.

"I am," responded Malik, burying his face in the crotch of her panties.

"I'm talking about Shoota," she clarified. "I know that's your homie, but he ain't your homie when it come to being the man."

Malik peeled away the edge of her panties and darted his tongue across her pussy. He was encouraged by the shallow shift of her body and her soft moan. Her fingers fell to his shoulders.

"Just be careful," she repeated in a soft breath of pleasure, her fingers digging into his flesh.

Her pussy grew wet on his tongue as he moved it across the fleshy mound. He squeezed her ass tight, enjoying the taste of her. He was filled with the mixed emotions of managing his aggressive friend, drug dealing, and the death of his grandfather.

Trinity nearly toppled over him as his tongue found its way inside her, stabbing and licking. She soon felt his hot tears on her body. Malik allowed Trinity to lift his face from her pussy, submitting to her soft kisses against his tears.

"It's okay, baby," she said softly, kissing his tears away.

Malik broke down sobbing, whispering how he would miss his grandfather and how life wasn't fair. Trinity's arms around him provided comfort as he purged his pain.

Chapter Thirteen

Perfect Aphrodisiac

It was hard leaving the house. Trinity did not want him to leave. *Your grandfather's funeral was just today,* she'd said. *And your mom ain't came out her room since we got back.*

Malik had to leave. Sitting in the house would only make him think of his grandfather. It wasn't until Malik promised to come pick her up after he dropped Shoota off did Trinity relax. She'd wanted to know where they would go. He promised her that he'd take her to a special spot and show her something she'd never seen before.

Malik could still see the look of anticipation on her face.

He still felt good about being able to put that smile there.

"Turn right here," said Shoota, pointing to a burger stand on the corner of 92nd and Hoover. "It's the third house on the right."

Malik knew that Roxanne would not approve of him exposing himself in this way. Being the man in the streets with the cocaine. He agreed that he could simply be courier and make decent money. *It'll be okay,* he said to himself as he pulled to the curb in front of a small white house with black grills on the windows. An electric blue candy painted '64 Chevy Impala on gold Daytons sat squatted on the dirt lawn.

"That's that nigga Shadow shit right there," said Shoota. "That muthafucka clean, ain't it?"

Malik was looking across the street where gang members were congregated on a porch, watching them. Malik was glad he didn't have any cocaine with him.

"Here he come now," Shoota said, ready to get out.

"Don't get out," instructed Malik.

Shoota frowned up. "This my nigga. He cool," he replied, his hand on the door lever.

"We gotta make this quick," Malik reminded him, only saying that he promised Trinity to be right back, neglecting to mention he had fifty kilos of cocaine to pick up.

"What's up groove," Shadow said, leaning to Shoota's window, his small dark eyes quickly scanning the interior of the car.

"This my boy, Malik," replied Shoota. "He the one got them chickens for fifteen."

Shadow looked to Malik doubtfully, not seeing any signs that he has access to a kilo of cocaine.

"Is that right?" said Shadow, moving a toothpick from one corner of his mouth to the other. "Where you from?"

"He don't bang. He live on my block," interjected Shoota.

Shadow frowned. "Damn nigga! Let groove talk for his self." Shoota looked to Malik before staring ahead.

"So, what's up? You got them birds, huh?" Shadow said to Malik.

"Yeh," he replied, seeing himself through Shadow's eyes. He didn't see a dope dealer, that's for sure.

"I can get one for fifteen myself. You can't give me a better deal?" asked Shadow.

Malik noticed Shoota become uneasy. He too felt the sly bargain. "That's the best I can do," he replied.

"You ain't got none I can test?" asked Shadow. "Shit might be some bunko you niggas got a hold to."

"Naw," Shoota said at length. "This shit straight off the boat."

"We can meet tomorrow. I'll let you check it out," offered Malik, regretting that he agreed to help Shoota out. He couldn't imagine surviving long dealing cocaine this way.

Shadow nodded. "Aiight, Malik. We can do that. You got a pager number?"

"Hit Shoota up. He'll let you know the place and time."

"What time about?" Shadow wanted to know.

"Probably in the morning sometime," replied Malik, unknowingly revealing to Shoota an approximate pick up for the dope.

Shadow tapped the door. "Cool. It's on. If it's straight I'll have fifteen for you."

Long after they'd left Shadow, turning down Hoover, Malik felt as if he'd made a mistake.

"My nigga," exclaimed Shoota, pounding his fist into his palm. "We can sew up the city. Ain't nobody got the plug we got!"

Listening to Shoota, Malik was sure he'd made a mistake. And when he thought it couldn't get any worse, Hill rolled up next to them in the black Cadillac. Al was in the seat next to him. Malik was glad they were on Shoota's side of the car.

"Wassup, cuzz," said Hill. "I got that for you."

Shoota smiled, then laughed mysteriously.

"What's so funny?" Hill wanted to know.

"I'm on!" Shoota shouted. "We got them chickens for fifteen. Half for eight!"

Malik wanted to reach over and punch Shoota in the mouth. He was thankful the light turned green at Florence.

"Holla at me!" yelled Shoota as Malik sped ahead. "Why you skirt off so quick?" Shoota asked Malik. "Them niggas be buying dope."

"I ain't tryna be out there like that."

"What you tryin' to do then, just go where that bitch tell you to go? It's money out here my nigga," hissed Shoota.

"Man, I'm not in it like that," Malik reminded him.

"Nigga, ain't no way you can get out now. You in so you might as well get yo' bread while it lasts."

Malik pulled up to Shoota's Cutlass on the block, happy to be rid of him. It was obvious to him that Shoota had a very different agenda. He had to laugh it off when Shoota suggested he tell Roxanne to put him in the game. He was absolutely certain now that he must keep Shoota away from her. She didn't trust him and he didn't like her.

"So, what time in the morning you gonna have that bird for Shadow?" asked Shoota, standing in the opened door.

"I'm not sure. I'll hit you in the morning," replied Malik.

"What you finna do now?"

"Gotta make a run before I pick up Trinity," said Malik.

Shoota grinned crookedly. "Ahhhh, my nigga already sounding like a boss!"

Malik made a U-turn in the middle of the street so that Trinity wouldn't see him pass by the house and more importantly, so Shoota couldn't guess where he was going.

Mario was standing at the entrance to the garage when Malik pulled into the auto repair shop. He approached to hand Malik the keys to the white Chevy Nova he'd pulled in beside.

Malik could feel the weight of the cocaine in the trunk. His scariest moment was when leaving the auto shop, fearing the sudden appearance of police to arrest him. Once he crossed the first street light on his way home he breathed easier.

Malik crept to a stop a few doors away from his house in case Shoota looked down the street. After skirting lawn edges to his front door to gather up Trinity he drove her to his special destination.

"This is serious, huh?" asked Trinity, referring to the new car. "So, where are we going?"

Malik smiled over at her. "You'll see."

Trinity relaxed, then asked, "So, you can just switch up cars any time you want?"

Malik nodded. "You'll see."

"Well, are we going to be able to eat at this special place you're taking me to?"

Malik frowned, having no idea if there was food at the stash house. "We can order pizza," he said to her delight.

The stash house was kept looking occupied by a regular gardener. Malik pulled to the back yard, out of sight from the street.

"Who's house is this?" asked Trinity, looking around the backyard with its lemon and orange trees.

"This Roxanne's stash house," replied Malik, lifting the spare tire from the trunk, revealing fifty kilos of neatly packed cocaine. Trinity gasped.

"Grab this bag," he instructed her, ignoring the incredulous look on her face.

She absently held the large canvass sac opened while

Malik filled it with bricks of cocaine.

Trinity was surprised to find that the house was furnished nicely with large sofas and a large television. She was standing over a money counting machine when Malik called to her from the hallway, having put away the cocaine.

The rear bedroom was complete with a bed and end tables. "Better than a motel," said Malik, flopping down on the bed. "And can't nobody hear us."

Trinity smiled, stepping into his embrace. "You gonna buy me a house like this one day?" she asked between kisses on his lips.

"Bigger," he promised, undressing her.

Trinity kneeled before him and took his tightening shaft in her mouth. She sucked him hard, making his body tense up. This only encouraged her, adding a twist of her head with each downward motion.

"Damn, baby," hissed Malik, unable to resist lifting her to the bed.

Trinity lay on her back, legs open to receive him. She exhaled slowly as he entered her tight pussy. She got even wetter with each gentle stroke, rolling her hips to match his motion.

Malik sucked on her thick nipples, first one then the other, losing himself inside of her. Fifty kilos of cocaine, a new borrowed car, and the promise of riches served as the perfect aphrodisiac.

Trinity was the first to hear a noise coming from the living room. Malik brushed it off. Trinity was sure there was someone in the house. She pushed him from her.

Chapter Fourteen

We Watchin' You

Roxanne was exhausted by a full day of hustlin' cocaine deals and managing her hair salon. She could see the salon from her office through a one-way mirror. The last of her clients was nearly out the door.

She was curious about a tall, pretty, dark-skinned woman whom she'd never seen before. Walk-in clients were usually told to make an appointment and turned away, but there was a last minute cancellation. Roxanne's head stylist, Nisha, agreed to tint her hair.

Roxanne was always interested to know who walked

into her salon, but this woman piqued her interest for the way she seemed to be clocking the movements of the salon. Added to this was the fact that the woman didn't seem at all comfortable with the idea of getting her hair tinted.

"Hello?" said the feminine voice tinted with masculine authority.

"Oh, sorry Pearl," replied Roxanne into the phone.

"I'm over here running my mouth and shit," complained Pearl.

Roxanne wanted to share how uninterested she was in the many love affairs of Pearl, but instead she said, "I'm sorry." She watched the woman occasionally look to the one-way mirror as if searching for something.

"It's cool," began Pearl, "so you got three for me? I can't deal with these dry spells, Roxy."

This got Roxanne's attention. "Of course."

"What's my price?"

"I can get you three for thirteen each."

Pearl was silent for a beat before she agreed. "So, can I seduce this young guy you sending to me? Is he cute?"

Roxanne grinned, her eyes on the suspicious looking woman. She seemed to be stalling, instructing Nisha to make small adjustments. "No, bitch. Leave him alone."

"Checking ain't cheating," chimed Pearl, sounding like a mischievous little girl.

Roxanne's desk phone signaled an incoming call. "Be ready tomorrow, girl. I gotta go."

There were two people left in the salon. The extra stylist, who had escorted her satisfied client to the secured door, was cleaning her work area. The suspicious woman was now fussing about the edges of her tint.

"*Hola*," said Mario in his clipped way. "Your guy has picked up his car," he announced.

Roxanne grinned into the phone, liking that Malik had

handled his part. "Thank you. See you in a few days," she responded, reminding herself to invest in a car phone for Malik.

"*Bueno*," agreed Mario.

Roxanne leaned back in her chair, studying the fussy client. Nisha was visibly frustrated. Roxanne rose, intending to see for herself what the fuss was about, but the ringing phone stopped her.

"Maximum Roxy," she said into the phone, watching another client being escorted to the door, leaving the suspicious woman.

"Maximum Roxy," she said again, but still without an answer. She hung up.

As she moved for the door the phone rang again. She exhaled with intended frustration as she answered the phone again. Harshly.

"Whoa, where's that sexy woman I know?" said Michael Concepcion.

"Hi, I'm sorry," she said apologetically. "Somebody been playin' on my phone."

"Probably the feds or a disgruntled employee," he replied seriously.

"Yeh, maybe. But what's scary is that my girls have been with me forever. Ain't nobody mad at me."

"I wouldn't say that," Michael cryptically replied.

Roxanne sat down, interested in what he wasn't saying. "I'm listening," she said soberly, watching the mysterious woman take her time inspecting her hair in the mirror.

"You know niggas was glad to see Tootie out the way," he began, "now niggas feeling you starting to push your weight."

"What niggas you talking about?" she asked, thinking back to Freeway Rick's visit.

"The streets in general. Benzo got respect in the street.

Now that he wrapped up expect the unexpected," said Michael.

Roxanne nodded, understanding the nature of the streets. She was quietly thankful for Michael's honesty.

"And lemme share something else with you," he began, "niggas speaking on a new connect giving up chickens for ten apiece."

Roxanne remembered this as the price she quoted Malik as a favor to Shoota. She shook her head in irritation at her misgivings being proven correct.

"So, be careful," added Michael. "I'm here if you need me."

"Thank you. I appreciate that," Roxanne said, watching the suspicious woman be the last client to head for the door, finally satisfied. "I'm coming to see you tomorrow," she added.

"Sounds like a plan."

Roxanne hung up the phone and walked out the office. Michelle, her favorite stylist and childhood friend, approached her.

"That one is a mess," said Michelle, pointing to the slim, pretty, dark-skinned woman just now leaving the salon. She was taking her time at the door, suddenly looking into her purse.

Just as suddenly she was pulled from the doorway and replaced by two men wearing ski masks. They rushed into the salon pointing large pistols at Roxanne and her three stylists. "Nobody move!" they shouted in unison.

Roxanne made a break for her office. The one-way mirror shattered following the crackle of a gunshot, freezing her in place.

"Freeze bitch!" the taller man shouted.

The shorter, stocky one dropped a duffel bag and pulled out a roll of duct tape.

"You bitches get on your knees!" commanded the taller man, swinging his black pistol in their direction. He then marched towards Roxanne while his partner in crime taped the hands and feet of her three stylists.

Roxanne suspected that the suspicious woman was a part of this, not confident that she'd call the police. She briefly envisioned herself knocking the gun from the man's hand, but his menacing glare behind the mask stopped her from attempting this superhero move.

"To the safe," the tall man demanded, waving the gun towards the office.

Roxanne reluctantly led the way, wishing she'd transferred all the money to the safe at the stash house. She hoped they would be satisfied with splitting the two thousand dollars she had in the safe.

"I hope you know what you're doing," Roxanne said, kneeling to the desk where she opened a cabinet to reveal the safe.

"Bitch! I know exactly who you are," the masked man responded, looking over her shoulder as she pulled the safe door open.

He shoved her aside, grabbing the .38 pistol on the top shelf. He then stuffed his pockets with the minimal left behind jewelry of customers. He flipped through the cash and looked at her with wide, disappointed eyes.

"Where the rest at, bitch?" he wanted to know.

It ain't here that's for sure, she thought to say, but instead said, "That's all we made for the day."

The shorter man joined them in the office, eyeing the money in the taller man's hand. "Is that it?" he asked.

"Yeh. Bitch say this all they get today."

"This bitch paid up. She got money somewhere," said the shorter man, looking around the small office.

"The silent alarm was activated when I didn't press the

code after the safe was opened," said Roxanne, hoping they were stupid enough to believe it.

"How much is that?" asked the shorter man, eyeing the money and appearing nervously wild-eyed.

"Couple thousand," his amateur crime partner replied, then he focused on Roxanne.

"Bitch, lay on your stomach," he said.

Roxanne did as he said, suspecting they'd duct tape her hands and feet, hoping for nothing more. When she felt no movement she rose up, catching a glimpse of them leaving with the purses of her three stylists.

Roxanne cut the women loose, promising to reimburse their day's earnings. Leaving the salon, she tried to place the two men who'd robbed her. No doubt they were amateurs, she assumed. It was nothing to pay her stylists back.

The episode had shaken Roxanne. She needed a remedy to calm down. She pulled into the driveway of the stash house, surprised to see the familiar red Chevy Nova parked in the backyard. She pulled in beside it, leaving the driveway free.

Roxanne expected to find Malik asleep, but when she heard the sexual moans of a woman she became instantly upset.

"Malik! What the fuck are you doing?" she screamed from the bedroom door as Malik sexed Trinity.

Malik looked up in surprise, not expecting that she would stop by.

"What the fuck is this?" she asked, though it was plain to see.

"It's just me and my girl," replied Malik, pulling on his pants while Trinity got dressed.

"This ain't no motel," Roxanne said, fully disappointed.

"Sorry 'bout this," apologized Malik.

"You ain't got to be sorry," added Trinity, brushing past

Roxanne in the doorway. "Take me home," she added.

Roxanne allowed her to pass without reply, catching Malik by the arm when he got to her. "Be back in the morning. We have business to discuss, among other things," she hissed, trying to control her anger and disappointment.

"Okay," responded Malik, choosing not to question her anger, yet resolving to get in a position to buy his own house.

Roxanne waited until Malik disappeared from sight down the street. She took a few deep breaths to calm her nerves. She peered out the windows with a mild suspicion that someone may be watching her. Satisfied that she was safe, she located the fifty kilos of cocaine in the closet of the front room.

She calmed herself at the sight of the raw powder. She cut a small slice into a brick and scooped out a tiny hill with her pinkie nail. She put it to her nose and inhaled. Her head reeled back and her throat cleared. Her eyes reddened and she felt light as air, all of her worries temporarily forgotten.

Chapter Fifteen

Infatuated

"She walked in on y'all fuckin'?" Shoota asked, howling with laughter as he bucked in the passenger seat.

Malik was driving on the 10 freeway eastbound to San Bernardino to meet with Pearl.

"She probably got y'all on film," added Shoota.

Malik didn't think it was a big deal, but apparently Roxanne did. Before sending him to meet Pearl she explained to him that all it took was for one person to tell another person and they'd lose what they couldn't pay for. By *they* she'd meant him personally. Malik got the point.

"Why you so quiet?" Shoota wanted to know.

"No reason," replied Malik, though he was thinking about his meeting with Pearl. This was his first out of town delivery.

"Did you ask her if she would give you better prices if it was you?" asked Shoota.

Malik shook his head, *No.*

Shoota seemed disappointed by this. "It's cool that the bitch put you on, but that bitch almost outta here."

"What you mean by that?" asked Malik.

"The feds bin on her. You know her nigga on death row and Benzo just got snatched up. If you ain't careful you gon' be next," warned Shoota.

Malik regretted bringing him now, but had to admit he felt safer with him.

"I already told you I'm just getting enough for basketball camp."

Shoota sighed. "Mannn, you can tell that lie to somebody else. You bin made enough already. This shit is addictive. Once you start gettin' it, it's hard to stop."

Malik silently agreed, deciding to show Shoota what Roxanne bought for him. "Reach to the back seat and grab that phone off the floor."

"Phone?" said Shoota before reaching behind him and pulling up a Mobira Motorola portable phone.

"Plug that cord into the cigarette lighter," instructed Malik. "She got one just like it in her car. You can walk around with it too," explained Malik.

"I bet the bill sky high," responded Shoota, snapping the phone receiver off the large battery pack. "Is it on right now?"

"Yeh, but don't make no call. I'm waiting on Roxy."

Shoota grinned wickedly. "So, that's what you calling her now, *Roxy?*"

"Why you so hard on her?" Malik asked. "She puttin' money in a nigga pockets. Real money."

"Yeh, but she just using you," replied Shoota. "She ain't gon' give you no dope on consignment and let you do your own thing."

I don't have my own thing, Malik thought to say, but instead said, "Nigga, doin' better today than I was yesterday."

"Can't argue with that," Shoota agreed. "That nigga Shadow didn't think we was gon' come through."

"He was thirteen hundred dollars short," Malik reminded him.

"That lil' shit ain't nothin'. He in the streets with it. He gon' get that back to us."

"He gonna get that back to *you*," corrected Malik. "That's coming out your half of the five."

Shoota agreed, patting his pockets. "They missin' that bread too," he said. "Ey, I gotta lil' college chick out this way," he added as they exited the freeway.

The ringing phone surprised them both. "Hello," answered Malik.

"Hi," replied Roxanne. "You made it yet?"

"Yeh. Just now," Malik said, feeling special being able to talk on a phone while driving.

"I sent Pearl's number to your pager. I'll be setting up a time for you to meet Joseph later."

"Okay," replied Malik, aware of Shoota's interest in his conversation.

"Okay, hun. Be safe. Call if you have a question. Now, I gotta go. These bills are expensive."

Shoota wasted no time in asking what she'd said, looking to Malik eagerly.

"Just setting up the meetings," replied Malik.

"We got time to meet these bitches?"

"Yeh. Call 'em." Malik listened as Shoota reached the

girl, smiling and assuring her that he was in a car on a phone and near where she lived.

The large apartment complex was clean and spacious. Not an old person or child's toy in sight. Young men and women lounged on balconies or in the courtyard near a large swimming pool.

"This for college students and shit," said Shoota, leading the way. "I met this chick when I was out here in a boys' home."

"Last summer?" asked Malik as they reached a second floor door facing the courtyard.

"Moms was trippin' off that shit. She hated she called the police on me."

Malik remembered how Shoota and his mom used to argue all the time, but not the reason. He was about to ask him when the door opened, revealing a chubby, blonde-haired white girl. She had a nice smile.

"Hi," she said, stepping aside to let them in. "I was so surprised to hear from you," she said to Shoota.

"This my boy, Malik," offered Shoota. "This Jennifer, my future wife," he added, smiling, making her giggle as she extended a soft hand to Malik.

"Pleased to meet you, Malik. Call me Jen," she said, but Malik's attention shifted to the dark chocolate, kente cloth-wearing woman who'd stepped from the kitchen.

Malik followed her with his eyes as she crossed to sit on a large couch, holding a bowl of ice cream.

"That's my roommate, Elisa," said Jen.

Malik felt an immediate connection with Elisa. She held his gaze until Shoota nudged him on the elbow to break the trance.

"What's that you're holding," asked Elisa, pointing her spoon to the Mobira portable phone in Malik's hand.

"Oh," he began shyly, "it's just a phone."

"Just a phone, huh," Elisa replied, her smile bubbly. "You rich or something?"

"He must be," Jen interjected. "My dad complains all the time about his phone bill. And he's a lawyer. You would think he shouldn't complain."

Malik had made his way to the couch while Jen talked, maintaining eye contact with Elisa across the thick carpet.

"So, what's the story?" asked Elisa, not moving from the center of the couch, forcing Malik closer to her.

"It was a gift," he replied.

"From a stalker girlfriend or are you a drug dealer?" she asked, giggling with her ironic humor.

Malik was tempted to tell her the truth, but Shoota interrupted their connection by asking Jen why her friend was being so nosey. Malik suspected Shoota was jealous. He was glad when Jen pulled him away, both disappearing into a hallway.

Elisa's shapely body couldn't be hidden by the kente wrap. The table before them is covered with opened textbooks and notepads.

"You in college?" he asked.

Elisa nodded. "You're tall. You play basketball?"

"Yeh," he replied. "I should be playing at USC next year."

Elisa smiled, her teeth white and dimples deep. Her hair flowed long and thick over her shoulders. "So, what's the story with the phone?"

Malik didn't want to lie. He'd forgotten Trinity and the common sense to keep his business secret. "Well, I'm out here to drop off some stuff to earn money for basketball camp."

"Drugs?"

Malik nodded, expecting her immediate judgment and disapproval.

"Are you a pretty good basketball player?" she asked, licking the ice cream from her spoon.

"Yeh. I made the McDonald's All-American team last year."

"You're still in high school?"

"I'm a senior," he replied, sure again that she'd break the spell of attraction between them.

"I'm a freshman at UC San Bernardino."

"So, you're into Black Power and stuff?" asked Malik.

Elisa giggled, leaning into the sofa, her legs tucked beneath her. "You're cute," she said, looking to him seriously now. "It's quite possible that all the ducks are flying in the wrong direction," she said cryptically.

Malik's pager buzzed on his hip. He felt her eyes on him as he checked the number. It was Pearl.

"Is that your drug drop off person?" asked Elisa.

"Yeh."

Elisa's radiant face brightened with mischief. "Aren't you afraid?" she asked.

"Naw," he replied, making up his mind to leave Shoota behind.

"Can I come?" she asked gleefully, bouncing a little and tapping his leg. "No, I'm just playing."

Malik rose.

"Are you coming back?" she wanted to know.

Malik whispered low, "I'm leaving Shoota here. I'll be back."

"Okay. Be safe, Malik."

The musical tone of Elisa's voice flowed inside of him. Her natural beauty was still before him as he listened to directions from Pearl to reach her on the car phone.

The U's, was what Pearl called the projects in which she lived. Just off California and U streets, it was one of San Bernardino's most dangerous places, the look of it reminding Malik that he didn't have a gun. He questioned his decision to leave Shoota behind.

Pearl directed him to her block, hidden in the vast sprawl of the projects. She looked nothing like he'd imagined. Standing with a group of men who made Shoota look like an elementary thug, her full breasts were the only things separating her from looking like them.

"Heyyy," cheered Pearl, separating herself from her posse when Malik pulled up. "Here's my new man."

There was no denying her status as the boss of these hardened thugs, her own demeanor both relaxed and stern. Dressed in khaki pants and flannel shirt, she was more man than most except for her soft smile and flashes of femininity.

"I think I'm going to like you," said Pearl once she'd tested the dope in the privacy of a nearby apartment.

The expensive furnishing contrasted with the outward appearance and dusty courtyard of the building.

Pearl produced a duffel bag containing ragged-bound bundles of cash.

"You can count it, but you'd be wasting your time," said Pearl. "Me and Roxy go way back."

Malik flipped through the money quickly before calling Roxanne to confirm delivery. It was the most money he had been accountable for and he felt the weight of his responsibility on the way out of the projects.

A giddy feeling overtook him on his way back to Elisa, eager to sit and talk with her.

Chapter Sixteen

Mind Playing Tricks On Me

Roxanne didn't know if it was a good thing or bad that Malik's grandfather wasn't present during the robbery; whether or not the crime would have been committed at all. One thing for sure, Roxanne was committed to hiring an armed security guard.

She waited patiently for the glass repairmen to finish installing a new one-way mirror. She sat alone in a hairstylist chair, having just confirmed Malik's drop off to Pearl. She dialed Joseph Mordecai.

"Greetings," answered the proper sounding club-owning drug dealer.

"Hi, Joseph. This is Roxy, confirming you'll be available today."

"Hello, Roxy. Sure. I'm here at a venue, setting up for LL Cool J. Have your guy call me. We'll arrange for him to stop by later."

Roxanne regretted not accepting Pearl's invitation to the concert. It was ironic that Joseph was the promoter.

"Will do, Joseph," she agreed, ending the call.

She escorted the repairmen to the door after they'd polished the one-way mirror and gathered up their tools. Just as she opened the door two men walk up, obviously law enforcement; Roxanne guessed FBI.

"Roxanne Reese," the shorter, white man announced, pulling his badge identification from his inside blazer pocket.

The taller, black man, behind mirrored aviator glasses, remained silently stern.

"Yes, how can I help you?" she asked.

"I'm Dick Mooney, with the organized crime unit of the Drug Enforcement Agency," he rattled off before introducing his partner as Tom Higgins.

Roxanne nodded politely, waiting for the warrant or arrest, her heart beating like two monkeys in a pillowcase.

"We'd like to ask you a few questions," said the white federal agent.

"Not without my lawyer present," she replied.

"We can arrest you for conspiracy to traffic narcotics and take you to jail," began Mr. Higgins, "or you can let us in to have a word with you."

Roxanne's throat went dry. She feared she'd faint as she stepped back to allow them inside.

"I see you've had a bit of an incident here," said the white man, squinting his eyes as if the sun was in them.

Roxanne stood aside to let them roam, seeing where they'd land. They both stopped in the middle of the room. Roxanne took a seat in the nearest chair by the door.

"You haven't been to see Benjamin, have you?" said the white man.

Benjamin, she repeated to herself, unable, unwilling to do the work for them.

"Benzo Al," chimed in the black agent, still wearing his mirrored glasses indoors.

"And?" she responded, ready for where this was headed.

The white man hoisted his pants up, though they weren't sagging. "How about Tootie," he said. "You haven't been to see him either."

"Once again, and?" she responded, exaggerating her boredom.

"Guess you're doing fine without them, huh," said the white man, staring at her as if trying to figure out his next best threat.

"Look," chimed in the black agent. "You can help yourself out here. Work with us. We'll work with you."

Roxanne looked away from the mirrored glasses, unable to see his eyes. She wanted to be angry, but the absurdity of their visit began a bout of laughter that doubled her over, bringing tears to her eyes. The two agents looked at each other, confused.

"Y'all got to be the dumbest," she laughed out, wiping away tears.

"This is no laughing matter," said the white agent. "You'd be surprised to know who's working with us. We can be a benefit."

Roxanne shook her head. "This what y'all came for?" she asked, relieved. "Well, I'm sorry, but y'all wasted a trip. If y'all don't mind I have a business to run. Please leave."

She got up, done with their antics and stood by the door. She was wordless as they slowly fell in step towards her.

"You're making a big mistake, sister," said the black agent, following his partner out the door.

"If you woulda took your glasses off maybe I woulda threw you a bone, brother," she responded with a sour grin.

Just when the black agent turned to take his glasses off she shut the door in his face. Walking to her office she let out a hoot of laughter, though her insides were empty with fear.

Roxanne canceled her appointments for the day, leaving the shop open for Nisha and her other two stylists to work. She was in much need of some thuggish affection and knew the right person to give it to her.

After picking up a kilo of cocaine from the stash house she headed to Watts and Michael Concepcion.

"You must have added on to your house," she said into her phone, parked outside the house he was raised in, except now it had a second floor and expanded garage for his many cars.

"There she go," responded Michael. "I'll come get you."

Roxanne was waiting outside the black grill fence, being watched by two huge, brown-eyed Rottweilers.

"You never met my babies, huh," Michael said, bounding off the porch, smiling, wearing cargo shorts and a wife-beater that hugged his muscular torso.

"No, I haven't had the pleasure," she replied, scooting by them as they watched her carefully, awaiting a command.

"They my pig alarms," he said, leading her inside the cool house of modern furniture.

"That's what I need at my salon," she said, deciding not to tell him about the DEA visiting her.

"They'll probably scare all your customers," he said, taking the paper bag wrapped kilo she'd pulled from her

Gucci bucket purse. "Nice color," he added, examining the cocaine.

"Don't you wanna test it?" she asked, sitting down on the couch.

"Naw. I trust you," he assured her, stepping towards the kitchen with the dope. "Want something to drink?"

"Any kind of juice. Hennessy if you have any," she responded, looking around the living room.

On the fireplace mantle were pictures of him with other men framing gleaming low-riders at car shows or in front of the house. On the walls were pictures of his mother who died from cancer a year ago. The living room was clean and orderly with plenty of plants hanging from the ceiling.

"Here you go," Michael said, returning with a glass of Hennessy. "Knock off that stress," he added.

"Thank you. How can you tell?" she said, the sting of the cognac feeling good going down her throat.

"What's going on?" he asked, relaxing against the couch to listen.

"Everything," she exhaled. "Mostly that I got robbed yesterday."

"Where at... by who?"

"Two men came into the shop. All they got was some change."

Michael thought of Benzo and how this wouldn't have happened if he was out. "You need security," he said.

"Just what I was thinking," she replied, taking a long sip of the cognac.

Michael watched her drain the glass, privately turned on and reminded of how close they used to be.

"There's something else I need, Michael," she said, her voice husky.

"What's that?"

"I need you to fuck me good."

That was all the invitation he needed. What followed was sweet sucking of plump breasts before she demanded he turn her over and fuck her on the couch doggy style. And this was the first position of many on his way to giving her what she wanted.

Chapter Seventeen

You Got Me Feelin'
Brand New

Shoota was upset that Malik left without him to do the deal with Pearl. Malik could tell this by his pouting manner when he returned to the apartment carrying the money he got from Pearl.

"What's that?" Shoota wanted to know, pointing at the backpack Malik had slung over his shoulder when Elisa let him in.

"Cheese. Cheddar. Cabbage. Bread," replied Malik, noting the energetic smile spread on Elisa's full, heart-shaped lips.

Shoota shook his head, crossing to the kitchen. "You gon' learn," he warned. "These streets will chew you up acting like you ain't green."

Malik resisted putting Shoota in his place. Instead he said, "This was nothing homie, I need you tonight when we roll to see LL Cool J."

Elisa and Jennifer swooned with the news. "Ooh, I love James Todd!" Jennifer said. "Are we all going?" she asked hopefully.

"Yep," replied Malik, enjoying Elisa's quiet admiration as she stepped to his side.

"You need me to put that in my room?" asked Elisa, taking the backpack from him.

"What you need me for that for?" asked Shoota, unable to hide his envy, his eyes following Elisa as she disappeared into the hallway.

"I got another deal tonight," he replied, his own temper running short with Shoota's ever-growing petty jealousy.

Shoota nodded, recognizing through Malik's stern reply his own enviousness.

Elisa returned to the mouth of the hallway. "Are you staying out there?" she asked Malik.

In answer, leaving Shoota looking after him from the edge of the kitchen, he joined Elisa, following her to her room. Her plump ass rocked gently beneath the kente cloth wrap dress. Malik inhaled her jasmine scent, turning into her room.

Above her mahogany four poster bed was a framed portrait of Malcolm X. Along the walls were various prints of young, chocolate-skinned girls at various forms of play, complete with ponytails, lace ankle socks, and giant smiles.

"I don't usually bring boys into my room," said Elisa, gesturing to a large bamboo backed chair in the corner.

Malik sat in the chair, wondering if she had a boyfriend. On a desk at the opposite corner of the room sat a modest stack of books. At his feet magazines filled a rack.

Elisa folded her legs under her as she sat at the edge of her high bed, facing Malik. "I sensed that you needed to get away from him," she said.

"Yeh." Sighed Malik, liking the intimate feel of her room. "He tripping right now."

"How long have you two been friends?"

"Since we was little," responded Malik.

"They say it be the closest ones to you."

This was not the first time he'd heard this. Malik refused to believe this about Shoota.

"This is a nice room," complimented Malik, not wanting to think about Shoota.

"Thank you. I got it from my daddy." She smiled with this. "So, tell me more about yourself."

"You have a boyfriend?" asked Malik.

"Why, you think I should have a boyfriend?"

Malik shrugged, enjoying her inviting nature. He liked that she was in college. She wore no makeup and was the kind of beautiful he'd never seen before.

"Well," she continued, "Jen says that I'm picky."

"What kinda guys you like?"

"I don't really have a type, but I do like tall and athletic guys. Smart and ambitious too."

"What don't you like?" he asked, held by the glimmer in her coal dark eyes.

"Guys who don't know what they want. Guys who can't treat me right."

"That doesn't sound so picky," said Malik.

"It's really about chemistry though."

Malik agreed with this, tearing his eyes from her deep gaze to look around her room. "You seem pretty deep," he said. "You probably scare guys away."

"There are some cool guys around, but I'm really focused on school," she replied, and noting the light of attraction dim in his eyes, she added, "but if the right guy comes along who knows."

"How long you and Jennifer bin friends?"

"Just since school last fall. She was looking for a roommate."

Malik wondered if Jennifer had many guys coming over and if Elisa hooked up with their friends. He was thinking of this as she jumped from the bed and turned on the radio at her desk. The rich voice of Bob Marley washed through the room.

Elisa turned to Malik. "You're welcome to stay, but I have to study now since we're going to the concert later," she said apologetically, adding, "Thank you, by the way."

"No biggie. Cool if I chill right here then?"

"Sure. There's juice and sandwich stuff in the refrigerator if you're hungry."

Malik relaxed in the chair, her slender back to him as she sat at the desk. The musical notes soothed him and the revolutionary words helped him to see into her soul. He liked her in a special way, felt her in a way he'd never felt a woman before.

Malik was awakened by a tap on the shoulder. He opened his eyes slowly. Shoota was standing over him.

"They got the concert on the radio. When we supposed to be there for the deal?" asked Shoota.

Malik looked around the room as he reached for his pager. Elisa was asleep on her bed, covered with a flower print sheer blanket. It was dark outside. Joseph Mordecai had left a page for him only thirty minutes before.

"Aiiite," Malik said in a low voice, grabbing his portable phone on the way out of Elisa's room.

Shoota stood by as Malik called Joseph to arrange where to meet at the concert. He felt Shoota's eager ears listening to the arrangements being made. Malik was pleasantly distracted from his presence by the tender stroke of Elisa's hand across his back on her way to the kitchen.

The women drove separately at the suggestion of Elisa, who reminded Malik that though she'd love to ride with him, there were drugs in his car. She said this without judgment.

"I know a few folks out this way who live in both the Meridian projects," said Shoota. "They paying a thousand dollars an ounce and twenty thousand for a bird."

Malik began to see the possibility of making some real money. With Shoota's connections they could be like Cookie, Donut, RL, or Money Bags.

"That bitch gotta let us get on though," continued Shoota. "Even if she give 'em to us for ten each we can get our bread. Break them bitches down and serve zones for a thousand. That's thirty-six thousand my nigga, more if we sell double-up."

Malik nodded absently, encouraging Shoota. He could see himself visiting Elisa. Having two girlfriends and two apartments. He'd have to continue giving Pearl her same price, he reasoned.

The Orange Show was an annual concert venue in San Bernardino that featured numerous outdoor food courts, games, and entertainers. Malik found the auditorium where LL Cool J was scheduled to perform. The concert atmosphere was electric with the anticipation of seeing LL Cool J. Malik left Shoota on the concert floor to meet Joseph Mordecai in an upstairs room overlooking the dance floor.

"Well now," cheered Joseph Mordecai from the middle of the sparsely furnished room when Malik entered.

Malik was shocked by the paleness of Joseph, his skin contrasting sharply with his black slick-backed hair and ice blue eyes. His thin frame was clothed in a shiny red Adidas tracksuit. Numerous gold rope chains hung from his slender neck.

"You've got a good look about you," said Joseph, looking to a burly man seated in a far corner. "Don't he, Jacob?"

The burly man nodded. Malik was sure that he had a gun tucked beneath his leather coat.

"I'm Joseph," said the pale man, extending his hand. "I already like you. I have good instincts. I trust my instincts." He smiled broadly, revealing very white teeth.

Malik shook his hand, noting its dry papery feel. Malik's only dealings with white people had been his coaches. Joseph was unlike any white person he'd ever seen.

"We've been looking forward to meeting with you," said Joseph, walking to the one-way mirror window to look at the growing crowd below. LL Cool J had taken the stage. Malik realized now that Joseph was mimicking LL Cool J's dress code. He found this humorous and interesting.

"I've got two hundred thousand dollars for you, Malik. But that's nothing. What's more is our message."

Malik turned to the pale man, wondering what the message might be.

"We're looking to expand our investments. Saul thinks you're someone we can count on."

Malik was confused. He'd never heard the name Saul.

"Saul is Roxanne's lawyer," Joseph clarified. "Word is she's on her way out. We're looking for someone who can pick up the pieces. We're talking about making you rich," he said, his words coming out close together.

Malik found Elisa. She was dancing alone without much movement, slow winding her body.

"You're not going to get rich being a courier or selling

to crack heads," said Joseph.

Malik nodded, imagining a richer rich than Shoota imagined. Richer than Freeway Rick. He imagined the kind of rich that came with a bodyguard, careless enough to imitate a rapper's dress code down to the gold ropes and spending two hundred thousand dollars like it was twenty.

"There are three networks," began Joseph anew, "us, the Colombians, and the people Freeway Rick in bed with. We own the banks. We have their money. Who'd you rather roll with?"

Malik nodded, trying to comprehend what was being asked of him. This only happened in the movies. He thought of Roxanne. She put money in his pocket. But maybe she was conveniently using him like Shoota said.

"Just be ready. Give it some thought. The two hundred grand could be yours shortly if you come on board when it's time. And that's just change."

"I hear you," responded Malik, feeling stuffed in the brain with a new potential reality that challenged his outlook. He was glad he'd left Shoota on the dance floor.

When Malik joined Elisa, coming up behind her to grab her in his embrace, he had two hundred thousand dollars in the trunk of the Chevy Nova. He was feeling bold and brand new in stature as he turned her to him. She turned her lips up to share a tender hypnotic kiss.

Chapter Eighteen

All In

Roxanne was feeling a sort of pressure she'd never felt before. She'd never experienced someone walking into her salon and robbing everyone inside. Hiring a security guard gave her pause, given the fact that the feds were watching. She feared they might send an agent to pose as an out of work security guard. She laughed at this possibility now, looking through the one-way mirror as Nisha set up her work station.

She also felt comforted by her recent meeting with Michael Concepcion. The warm feeling of their lovemaking was still with her. The hard fucking was what she'd wanted. The tender lovemaking afterwards was what she'd needed.

Michael's suggestion that they unite to take over the city and branch out to other states pushing major weight intrigued her. Though she had been setting up more out of town connects, Michael offered more options on the east coast and in the south.

Roxanne had always been aware of the potential benefit of their union, but the time had never been right. She resolved to take it slow, enjoying her independence.

When Nisha moved to the door Roxanne suspected that it was her morning client, but was surprised to see Dale Dog from Main Street Crips. His trademark sinister grin pushed Nisha back, who looked nervously to the one-way mirror.

Roxanne pushed down the nervous feeling in her stomach. First it was Freeway Rick, sniffing around to pick up clients Benzo's arrest may have scared away.

With Dale was his homeboy Droop, named for the way his left eyelid hung low. Roxanne stepped from her office just as Nisha's client walked in warily behind the two gang members.

"How may I help you?" asked Roxanne. Through the front glass she could see Dale's pearl white convertible Impala parked near the street.

Dale grinned, dressed casually in blue khakis and a white t-shirt. "Wassup, Roxy," he replied, eyeing the curvaceous woman sitting in Nisha's styling chair.

"Wassup, Roxanne," added Droop, sitting in an empty chair. "Tell Tootie I send mine," he added, relaxing.

"I came to holla at you real quick," said Dale, approaching Roxanne.

"Okay," she responded warily, aware of his reputation as a smooth talker and hood reputable.

They both wore the customary large Turkish ropes.

Their jheri curls glistened under the shop lights.

"You doing alright for yourself I hear," he said, following her into the office.

It's the *'I hear'* part that put her on guard. "What you hear?" she asked, sitting at her desk.

Dale took a quick glance around the office, reminding Roxanne that he had often been there to meet Tootie for business. He turned to look through the one-way mirror. Droop was leaning in the chair, talking to Nisha's client.

"That boy is a cock hound," Dale said, turning back to Roxanne with a sly grin.

Roxanne was not surprised to see the woman writing her number down on a piece of paper.

"Tootie straight?" asked Dale, looking to Roxanne.

"Yeh, he's cool," she replied. "We should know something about a new trial soon."

Dale shifted in his seat. "I hate to see that happen to my guy," he said, giving a quick shake of his head.

Roxanne let the silence grow pregnant, waiting for him to get to his point.

"Birds twenty grand right now," said Dale, looking at her with new eyes. "Ever since Tootie left it ain't been the same."

"You don't like the prices?" she asked, sure that he was benefiting.

Dale's brown eyes sparkled. "I'm getting mine off with no problem, but I hear some getting they chicken for thirteen." His eyes grew big with disbelief.

Now Roxanne understood. To hear someone had bought a kilo for thirteen threatened his hustle.

"Tootie woulda never sold one bird for that," he added.

"What all this gotta do with me?"

Dale grinned knowingly. "Come on, Roxy," he began, "niggas couldn't wait to whisper that shit. Yo' new boy in traffic fucking with people I know you wouldn't never fuck with. And fasho not giving birds up for thirteen."

Roxanne wondered if Freeway Rick had something to do with this meeting. She recognized It was not her business if Dale got his cocaine from Freeway, but she was interested in how much weight he was moving.

"Well, let me say this," she said. "What I do is my business. Now, if you want to talk about business we can do together, I'm all ears."

Dale smiled with a new glint in his eyes. "What numbers you talkin'?"

"That depends, Dale. How many you tryna get?" she said, privately thrilled.

She'd thought of approaching him, but needed the right opportunity. It was no secret that Dale operated many dope houses and had put on all the Main Streets who were about money.

"Shit," he hissed. "That depends. What a hundred grand get me?" he asked.

Roxanne estimated that he might be getting ten kilos and doubling, even tripling his investment by breaking some down for his dope houses.

"Fifteen," she responded, figuring a twenty-five hundred dollar profit on each kilo was worth a new client.

Dale grinned. "I figured Tootie left you with his plug..." He was interrupted by Roxanne's look through the one-way mirror.

Malik strode into the office behind Roxanne's other two hairstylists and two clients. Shoota was with him.

"That's your new boy, huh," quipped Dale, guessing.

Roxanne noted Malik's new d-boy swagger. She smiled inwardly. He had a new street confidence to go along with his new clothes and shining gold herringbone necklace anchored by a gleaming dollar sign.

"So, what's up. When you want it?" she wanted to know.

Dale nodded subtly. "I'm ready when you are."

"I'll have it for you tomorrow," she said.

Dale lifted himself from the seat. "We gonna have to have lunch or something," he said. "I got some other business I wanna discuss."

"Sure," she replied. "Let's get with this business first though."

He smiled with this, leading the way out the office. Approaching Malik, he nodded respectfully, though taking his measure. Droop joined Dale, the two making a sharp contrast in maturity and street stature in comparison to Malik and Shoota.

Roxanne ignored Shoota's inquiring stare as she invited Malik to join her in the office.

"Is that your basketball camp money?" she asked, pointing at the wide gold necklace around his neck, trying to hide her disapproval at his flashiness.

Malik unconsciously touched the gold dollar sign pendant. "It's just a little something," he responded.

"That little something will get you pulled over with a hundred kilos of dope in the trunk," she warned.

Malik thought of Joseph Mordecai and his promise to make him rich. But this was when Roxanne was out the way. He wondered how this would happen, privately conflicted with whether or not to share their conversation with her.

"How are you?" she asked, noting the hint of new exposure to money in his face. She suspected that basketball camp would fade.

"I'm good," he replied.

"And him?" she said, looking through the one-way mirror at Shoota, her disapproval unmistakable.

"He's cool." Malik thought to tell her about their argument, but decided against it. Shoota was again upset

115

that he'd missed being a part of the meeting with Joseph Mordecai. "I want to buy my own dope," he spat out, regretting that it didn't come out as smooth as he'd imagined.

Roxanne studied him casually, doubting that these were his words. She silently calculated how long before he was of no longer use. "We'll have to see about that. There's more to it than just having dope to sell," she said, adding, "You don't plan to go to basketball camp?"

Malik nodded, much too quickly, remembering Trinity's reminder of going to camp. "Yeh. I'm going," he assured her.

Roxanne leaned back, doubting he'd go. "You ready to make another run?"

"San Berdu?" he asked, hopefully, thinking of seeing Elisa again.

"Yes. Joseph and Pearl again. I've got someone lined up in Spokane."

"Washington?"

"Yep," she responded.

Malik nodded. "Is Benzo gettin' out?" he asked.

"Hopefully soon."

Malik resisted asking if Benzo would take his place when he got out. Instead he said, "Maybe I can have my own clients... like handle all the people from San Berdu and get my own clients."

Roxanne heard Shoota talking. This wasn't the Malik she'd come to know through his grandfather. "That might work out," she said, suddenly realizing that she was going to have to find a way to get Shoota out of the way. "So, in the meantime we have to get another car from Mario for your trip," she added.

Malik nodded. "Okay." He was excited about seeing Elisa.

"And don't wear that chain," she reminded him as he got up to leave.

Chapter Nineteen

Mixed Emotions

Malik appreciated Shoota's knowledge of the streets. Shoota knew all the people from every neighborhood who mattered. How he knew, Malik didn't question.

But Malik also understood Shoota's need to be involved, but this was weighted against his uncontrollable tendency to jealousy. Malik blamed this jealousy on his sense of duty to their friendship; a fear of being left out and left behind.

These thoughts traveled through Malik's mind as Shoota proceeded to inform him who exactly Dale Dog was and what that must mean about who Roxanne truly was and what she represented, in case he didn't already know.

"That nigga Dale Dog... mannn," Shoota exclaimed, looking out to passing traffic, no doubt impressed by having been in such close proximity to such a hood reputable.

"You think he be fucking with Freeway Rick?" asked Malik, remembering seeing him on Crenshaw with his friends and their shiny cars.

"Prolly so," replied Shoota. "All them niggas be fucking with each other. That's how they be keeping shit on lock."

Malik felt himself swell with the knowledge that Joseph Mordecai was on another level. This knowledge motivated him to keep Shoota separated from his business with Roxanne.

"Did you talk to the bitch about selling us another kilo for ten thousand? I got a new customer."

"She said she gon' think about it."

Shoota frowned up his face, thoroughly disappointed. "Fuck she mean... think about it?" he hissed. "She did it once already!"

Malik ignored his friend's pouting, thinking that Roxanne must have her own reasons. He resisted telling Shoota of his conversation with her about supplying his own clients even when Benzo got out.

"That bitch tryna hold us back. She tryna keep you as her errand boy. These little crumbs she paying you ain't shit!"

Malik was glad when he reached Shoota's car. He was beyond the mood of being able to agree with Shoota.

"What you 'bout to do?" asked Shoota, looking to Malik, the passenger door ajar.

"Finna go get my girl," responded Malik.

Shoota looked doubtful. "You ain't gotta get no more work for the spot?" he asked.

Malik shook his head. "Naw," he answered without conviction. "That shit ain't ready."

Shoota looked up the street before turning back to Malik. "Alright homie," he said. "Be careful."

"Always. I'll check with you tomorrow. We might be going to San Berdu in a minute," said Malik, throwing him a bone.

Malik accepted dap offered by Shoota and pulled off, turning in the street, sure that Shoota would question why he was going in the opposite direction of his house. He relaxed in the comfort of the Chevy Nova and unhooked the receiver of his portable phone from its cereal box sized battery.

"Hello?" answered the new and college-prepped voice of Elisa.

Malik couldn't help the smile that spread across his face and the way his heart fluttered.

"Hey," he replied awkwardly.

"How are you?" she asked calmly.

Malik wondered if he was being overly enthusiastic. "I'm good. I might be coming out there this week," he offered, hoping for some excitement in her voice.

There was a beat of silence, threatening his hopes, before she said, "I really enjoyed meeting you and look forward to seeing you again."

Her reply was refreshing. He was shook by her lack of mystery and teasing to be chased. He was smiling into the phone as he told her that he enjoyed meeting her too.

"Will it be for just a day?" she asked.

Malik hadn't considered staying more than a day, but said, "Yeh. I might do that. Maybe get a room."

"Sounds great," she replied. "Maybe it'll have a little stove kitchen. We could get groceries and play house."

He was surprised by her intentions, never imagining that she would plan to join him, though when mentioning it he'd hoped so.

Mario's Auto Repair loomed nearby, its familiar plain sign marking its greasy landmark. "Cool," he agreed, pulling into the auto shop and parking in an empty spot next to a similar Chevy Nova. "I'll call you later. I gotta handle some business right now," he added proudly.

"Okay, hun," she said.

Malik ended the call, hearing her say *hun* again in his head just as Mario walked up, smiling under his large mustache.

"Ohhh," Mario teased. "She must be good my friend, no?" he said, shaking Malik's hand as he got out the car.

Malik had to admit to himself that Elisa felt good to him. There was something new and exciting about everything about her. She represented a wider vision. Wholesome and natural.

"Things are good, no?" said Mario, handing Malik the key to the black Chevy Nova he'd parked next to.

Malik replied, "Everything good, my friend." Feeling closer and more familiar with Mario.

He often suspected that the genial Mexican wished to engage him in a more personal conversation, but refrained out of respect for Roxanne. He held onto this feeling, confident that one day he'd be trusted enough to establish his own deal if necessary; he remembered what Joseph Mordecai said about Roxanne one day being out the way.

Malik called Trinity on his way to the stash house— experiencing a private thrill with his load of cocaine and talking on his portable phone.

He wondered if the pretty girl in the Corolla next to him suspected he was a drug dealer. When her eyes traveled to the gold chain and dollar sign, he was reminded of Roxanne's warning to take it off.

"Where you at, baby?" asked Trinity. "You on your way?"

"Yeh. I'm finna make a quick stop and come scoop you," he said, ignoring the friendly wave of the girl in the Corolla.

"Okay. Your mom isn't feeling good. She ain't cooked or nothing," said Trinity.

Ever since the funeral Malik's mother had mostly stayed in her room. The last time he had checked on her she had been in bed under the covers. Though she said she was okay, she lacked motivation to get out of bed.

"She gotta go back to work next week. She just prolly tired," he responded, hoping this was the case.

Trinity sighed. "You should bring her something to eat. I'm hungry too."

Malik turned the corner, the stash house in view at the middle of the quiet street.

"Okay. I'll stop and get some KFC." He could feel her hesitation with something else to say. He hoped it wasn't bad news.

"Malik," she said low.

Malik slowed near the driveway. "Yeh," he replied.

"How would you feel if I was pregnant?"

Malik stopped the car in mid-turn into the driveway. Silence filled the space between them.

"Baby?"

"You pregnant?"

A beat passed before she said, "I think so. I'm late and I threw up this morning. Maybe I should go to the doctor first to be sure."

Gone was her expectation of Malik's happiness. He felt the sadness in her voice. "I hope it's a boy," he said, liking the feeling of the smile coming through the phone as his pager buzzed on his belt.

"Me too," she responded. "Maybe we can pick up a pregnancy test from the store before we go to the room."

"Sounds like a plan," replied Malik, easing to the back

of the driveway. "Let me drop this yayo off at the spot. I'm on my way."

"Okay, baby."

Malik felt as if he was on a cloud when he called Roxanne, responding to her page.

"Hey, Roxy," he said, his smile big.

"You sound happy," she responded. "What's up?"

"Oh, my girl pregnant. She think. We gotta get a test."

"Oh! That's great! You're happy it sounds like," she said, wanting to mention how a new child replaced the death of a loved one.

"Yeh, it's cool."

"Well, I'm happy for you. I have some good news for you myself," she began, "I put an extra brick in the car for you. It's worth more than what I give you already. So, if you got people you wanna look out for and get your money then it's up to you."

Malik had mixed feelings about this. There was the fear of actually selling his own dope and the risks involved. And then there was the opportunity to make more money.

"That'll work," he responded.

"On one condition," she added seriously. "You don't sell to people I introduce you to."

"Got you," he replied, looking in the rearview mirror, wondering if he just saw the back of Shoota's Cutlass pass by slowly. He pulled further into the backyard, out of sight.

"I'll be by the spot later. You don't have to stay. You can leave your brick there until you need it."

"Thanks. I'm about to put the stuff in the house now," he said, out of the car and walking back up the driveway for any sign of Shoota's car.

Chapter Twenty

Legitimate Dreams On Hold

Roxanne was happy for Malik. A new baby was a blessing. And even better he would feel the need to make more money. Basketball camp would have to wait. She smiled with this selfish thought.

Cocaine was an addiction not only for the user, but also for the supplier. Dreams could be achieved, deferred, as well as destroyed. Cocaine had the unique ability to accelerate friendships and destroy long-lasting relationships. Betrayal and loyalty were at constant odds.

Roxanne's thoughts were interrupted as she looked

through the one-way mirror where Nisha chatted easily with a client. Her two other stylists were just as busy with clients in their chairs.

"Maximum Roxy," she answered.

"Good evening," replied Saul, sounding as if it was hard for him to breathe.

"Hi, Saul," said Roxanne. "You better get that checked out. You don't sound so good."

"Years of fine cigars," he complained. "Good living has its price."

"You're right about that," she agreed, thinking of her own private indulgences.

"Joseph is both impressed with your product and your young courier."

Roxanne was glad to hear this. She'd forgotten to ask what role Shoota played in the deal. She wondered if Malik allowed him to be present.

"Well, I have a good feeling about him," she responded, feeling confirmed in her decision to invite Hill for a private meeting.

"He's so impressed that he wants to make sure he sees him again when he delivers the next shipment."

"I wouldn't have it any other way. He didn't mention seeing his friend, did he?"

Saul chuckled hoarsely. "He did mention he was good with the ladies. Your young courier arrived with two ladies and another young guy. He left them on the concert floor to handle the deal," said Saul, adding, "real classy businessman."

Roxanne was pleased; proud of the effect Malik had had on Joseph Mordecai. "He's a good kid."

"Roxy," Saul began, "he's the real deal according to Joseph. With everything that's going on you thought of laying back and letting Malik handle things?"

Roxanne saw Hill walk into the salon with his brother Al. *Now is not the time to lay back,* she thought to herself.

"He's playing the position I need him to play, Saul," she said, thinking to add that he might want to stay in his lane and not dictate how she should run her business.

"Well." He sighed. "Just thought I'd throw that out there."

"Well, I appreciate your concern, but I can handle my own business," she said. "What I need from you is to get my husband off of death row and out of jail. And I need a better bail for Benzo."

"I'm working on it," he assured her. "It's hard to make deals with the feds watching so closely. Believe me when I say that my business is suffering."

Roxanne felt a note of disloyalty in his tone.

"But I'll do whatever you want, Roxy. You know that," he added.

Roxanne didn't believe him, though she couldn't put her finger on the reason for this feeling. But seeing Hill was the first step in securing her investment in Malik.

"I hear you, Saul," she said. "Tell Joseph I appreciate his business. I'm ready for him. Malik will meet with him shortly."

She hardly responded to Saul's extended goodbye as she ended the call. She stepped from the office and showed herself to a waiting Hill. She gestured him to her office.

Hill was dressed in his customary soiled khaki pants and white t-shirt. His silky black hair hung in loosely twisted braids from the back of his Dodgers baseball hat.

"What it do," he said, plopping down in the seat beside her desk.

He'd never confirmed or denied any knowledge that Mitch was a federal agent. It was enough for Roxanne, and luckily for Hill, that he agreed to make things right when called upon in return for Benzo being arrested. After all, it was Hill who recommended Mitch to her.

"I need your help," she said. "I got this dude who might be a snitch."

The irony of this gets his attention. "Who you talking about?"

"He be hanging around one of my guys and I can't trust him," she said, looking for any sign that this might be a bad idea. "You know a dude called Shoota, be on 41st off Menlo?"

"Aww, yeh," replied Hill, almost admitting they'd done business together. "What you need?"

Roxanne studied Hill for a second before she said, "I need him killed."

Hill wanted to laugh out loud. Owing her for Benzo being locked up was one thing, but killing someone was another. "What's in it for me?" he asked.

"You owe me."

"Benzo ain't dead," he said, shrugging. "I mean... you want me to kill a nigga."

"You ain't never killed nobody before?"

"You kill the nigga if you think it's that easy," he said.

Roxanne was looking through the one-way mirror when she asked, "What would it take?"

"Shit," he hissed, looking around the room as if for hidden microphones. "Hypothetically speaking I'd be straight with a few birds," said Hill, looking to her seriously.

Roxanne nodded, calculating that it represented $15,000 for her and $60,000 for him if he sold the bricks whole, more if he broke them down.

"You got it," Roxanne assured him.

Hill held up a finger. "I ain't saying I'll do it. This hypothetical," he said.

"Sure. Now, hypothetically when?"

Hill grinned, exposing a cracked front tooth. "Hypothetically, whenever the nigga ain't around no more."

Roxanne smiled inwardly. It was the best she could have hoped for. "I can work with that," she said, standing. "I'll throw in an extra one if it's sooner rather than later," she added.

"Hypothetically," he reminded her, leading the way from the office.

Roxanne chatted it up with her stylists, giving Hill time to leave before leaving herself, adding nothing to the gossip about Eddie Murphy having a baby by a popular woman they'd gone to high school with.

She drove to the stash spot, preparing to meet with Donut, who was a hood reputable from Rollin' 90s Crip. It was her plan to sew up the city one hood at a time. Cookie also planned to stop by for ten kilos. She was privately giddy with her recent accomplishment, aware perhaps these men having hopes of forming a more intimate, sexual partnership, but reminded herself to maintain her independence.

Propositioning Hill for murder was both risky and potentially rewarding. She trusted her instincts and was looking forward to a long-term relationship with Malik; and she saw Shoota as a potential threat to her vision.

The street was quiet, just the way she liked it. As she pulled into the empty driveway she was unaware of the primered '79 Cutlass parked near the corner. She had no idea that Shoota had been there since Malik left, waiting to see if she would show up.

She pulled to the backyard, parking out of sight. She was proud of Malik, finding that he had moved the cocaine with obvious care and followed her instructions to keep his movements private.

Roxanne located the bricks of cocaine in the closet of the rear room. She took a kilo of cocaine and placed it on the dining room table. Tearing a small slice through the rice paper wrapping she lifted a chunk of powder from the brick. She broke down the powder and made several lines on a plate. The first line she snorted through a hundred dollar bill forced her head back and caused a sneezing fit with watering eyes.

She smiled, satisfied, saving the rest for after she'd handled her business.

Chapter Twenty-One

Surrounded By Snakes

"What if a nigga get cracked?" questioned Shoota, looking to Malik with wide eyes. "That bitch gon' come get a nigga?"

Malik nodded, having heard this from Shoota for the second time during the drive.

"You act like this shit gon' last forever," continued Shoota. "Nigga gotta think about that shit. That bitch playin' a nigga, homie. I'm tellin' you."

"She paying the lawyer to get Benzo out though," responded Malik.

"That nigga ain't never getting out! Look how long it's

bin, my nigga. The lawyer must ain't shit."

Malik silently agreed with this. If Benzo wasn't out by now then maybe the lawyer wasn't that good.

"What if they don't want him out?" asked Malik, thinking of Joseph Mordecai's words about Roxanne being soon out the way. If the lawyer was involved then it made sense that he would not work hard to get Benzo out.

Shoota looked to Malik, confused. "Then she a snake bitch just like ah been tellin' you, my nigga," he said. "If a nigga gon' get caught up a nigga need to get his bread right. And to do that a nigga need to be serving his own dope. Openin' up his own spots."

Malik pulled the receiver from the case and called Elisa. "We downstairs," he said quickly.

"Thas a fine black bitch," said Shoota about Elisa.

Malik grinned, wondering when he'd ask about what he would do about Trinity. "Roxanne gave me a kilo to work," he said.

"For whatever?" asked Shoota, wide-eyed in surprise.

Malik nodded, getting out the car.

"Nigga! We might as well sew up a few spots. I know exactly where to go," said Shoota excitedly, catching up to Malik on the pathway to Elisa and Jennifer's apartment. "I'll have that shit sold in one day and set up a spot to get rollin!"

Elisa was standing in the doorway when they reached the bottom of the steps. Her white smile against her dark skin shocked Malik, seeing the natural beauty that made his mouth tighten. Shoota's speech was arrested, following Malik's gaze up the steps.

Elisa gave a small wave, her smile narrowing. "Are you two going to just stand there?" she asked, her body rocking with a soft giggle.

"This bitch," whispered Shoota, starting up the steps first.

Malik watched her deep black eyes as he climbed the steps. They held Shoota for an instant before falling on him, sending a small electric shock through him.

"Hey you," she said when Malik met her on the landing, Shoota having walked inside the apartment.

"Hi," Malik replied almost bashfully. "Shoota said you fine," he added, feeling a need to apologize for him referring to her as a bitch.

Her eyes dulled as she said that was nice of him, then sparkled when she added, "What do you say?"

"You're like Africa," replied Malik, adding, "like those pictures of beautiful women that be on the walls at school."

Her head bowed with a soft giggle. "Well, I am part Nigerian. My mother is Hawaiian," she offered.

Malik couldn't help but to think that mixture created the most beautiful smooth ebony skin and long endless eyelashes.

"How long are you staying?" she asked, her eyes quickly passing over his new gold herringbone chain, turning to walk indoors.

"Maybe 'til tonight," he replied, wanting to take the chain off. He resisted asking her if she liked it.

Shoota and Jennifer were absent. Malik followed Elisa into her room, his pager buzzing on his belt. Elisa turned to him at the door and wrapped her arms around his neck, interrupting his motion to look at his pager. She kissed him on the lips.

"Why you need a pager when you have that phone?" she asked, looking to the portable phone hanging in his grip.

"Costs money to get calls."

Elisa nodded with understanding, tapping the gold dollar sign at the end of his necklace. "Well, handle your business," she said, walking to the desk where open books lay. "I have to finish a paper."

Sitting in the large bamboo chair opposite Elisa, Malik pulled the necklace over his head as if relieving himself of a huge burden. He dropped it carelessly to the carpet.

Calling Joseph Mordecai and hearing his enthusiastic welcome made Malik feel as if he was a member of an exclusive club. Before him, Elisa's slender back in a Black Panther t-shirt was an ironic addition to his feeling of welcome.

"Hello, my friend," said Joseph.

Malik was reminded of the way Mario greeted him only yesterday while exchanging cars, with a measure of warmth that felt like a newfound trust.

"How's it going?" replied Malik, looking to Elisa, liking the way her hair fell as she bent her neck to write, one hand rising to cup her chin.

Joseph smiled through the phone. "Life's good, Malik, my friend. I've got a few friends over at my girlfriend's house. Swing on by," he said. "Bring your girl if you want. We've got food on the grill!"

Malik smiled when Elisa looked up at him. "Sounds good. I'll see if she can make it," he said, more for her ears. She turned to him fully, a pen at the corner of her lips.

Joseph instructed Malik on how to get to his girlfriend's house, not far from where they were.

"You know where Lytle Creek is?" Malik asked Elisa when he ended the call.

"Yes. It's in the hills. They're mostly vacation cabins and forest up there. Why?"

"Well, I have a meeting there today," Malik said casually, adding, "he said for me to invite my girlfriend."

Elisa raised her eyebrows. "Sounds serious," she said with a note of humor, adding, "bringing a girlfriend and all."

Malik smiled with her exaggerated expression. "You wanna roll?"

Elisa walked over to him and sat on his lap. She stared into his eyes as she said, "Malik, I trust my instincts. I like you. I'll go with you, but it doesn't mean I'm a fool about life or have any misconceptions about what you do. All I ask is that you protect me."

"I'll have drugs in the car," he said.

"This will be the first and last time, okay?"

Malik nodded, thrilled she'd decided to roll with him.

"Besides, I need to get out," she said, bouncing off his lap. "My brain is about to explode." She picked up his necklace. "You want me to put this up for you?" Malik grinned, standing to embrace her in a hug. She smelled like jasmine.

"You gonna let Shoota know you're leaving?" she asked.

Malik considered this for a moment before he replied, "Naw. Let's roll."

Sometimes a drive was more than a drive. Malik felt the slow unfolding of his soul during the conversation Elisa so expertly mediated between them. When she told him that she'd never dated a drug dealer or anyone younger than herself, he was not sure if she was letting him down easy.

He waited for the moment when she asked if he had a girlfriend, but it never came. He liked her more for this. He'd never met a woman like her before. She accepted him as he was, without judgment or a need to direct him except through skillful negotiation, as with the herringbone necklace.

He wasn't surprised when she shared the fact that her family was wealthy, but she cared nothing for money. Malik couldn't help but to think that wealthy people had the luxury of not caring about money. He resisted questioning her about her reasons for liking him, given the fact it seemed they were exact opposites. He wondered if this was a sort of rebellion for her. He'd never been with someone like her before.

"It's nice up here," said Elisa as they turned onto a graveled, sloping road at the shallow base of Lytle Creek.

To the left was a meandering stream, crackling under a log bridge.

Malik was listening to Joseph Mordecai on the phone. "Across that bridge and right after the market is where you turn," he said to Elisa.

The bridge narrowed to a cobbled stone way, with room for one car. The market was on a wooden rise, hidden behind large trees. Elisa made the right.

"I see it," Malik said into the phone before ending the call. He looked to Elisa, holding up the receiver. "Should I take this?"

The house spanned one side of the short tree-lined block behind the market. Gleaming foreign cars were parked like Monopoly pieces along the dirt curb. Joseph Mordecai appeared ahead, at a break in the cars.

"I think it'll be safe in the car," she responded, smiling to him.

"Good afternoon," said Joseph, looking across Elisa to Malik.

"This is Elisa," replied Malik.

Joseph swung his sparkling blue eyes on her. "Glad you could come," he said, waving to the spot behind him. "Pull in here."

Elisa pulled to a stop behind a cocaine white Rolls Royce. Beyond the lawn, standing on a wooden porch were a group of sharply dressed white people. There was a square looking black couple with them. Everyone was drinking from champagne glasses or foreign beer from the bottle.

"My girlfriend is inside," said Joseph, leading Malik and Elisa through the group, nodding and introducing them as his friends. Everyone smiled and tipped their drinks as they passed into the house.

"Your house is beautiful," Elisa said as they stepped off the foyer into a sunken space.

The house was bathed in sunlight. The entire back wall was glass, looking out to a glimmering swimming pool. Beyond was a descending tree line. Malik imagined the creek ran at the bottom of the drop off.

"It's my girlfriend's house," Joseph replied, waving his arm to a thin blonde woman just then peeling herself away from a group studying a wall painting.

Malik stole a glance at Elisa, getting the impression she was familiar with this kind of living. She turned to him suddenly and smiled easily.

Joseph introduced his girlfriend as Becky, but Malik would only remember how her skin resembled porcelain and her hair was wheat blonde.

"Pleased to meet you," said Becky, extending a thin, jeweled hand to Elisa. "Your skin is beautiful," she added.

"Bring us a few drinks," Joseph said to Becky, motioning Malik to a wide hallway. When Malik looked to Elisa, she was telling the girlfriend about the twined leather bracelet on her wrist. It was apparently something she picked up when she went to Brazil last summer.

"Come on, they're fast friends," said Joseph, tapping Malik to follow him.

The walls of the hallway were lined with photos of smiling people dressed for climate in various parts of the world. They turned into a room streaked with sunlight filtered in by the trees in the front yard.

Joseph lifted a backpack from behind a wet bar. On the bar next to it, he placed a plain white box the size of a large Bible. "That's two hundred thousand," he said, looking to the backpack.

He pushed the box to Malik. "This is a gift. For you. From me," he said, first pointing at Malik, then himself.

Malik lifted the lid on the box. Inside was a gleaming chrome gun.

"That's a four-four Magnum. Clean. Registered to a private company. If you ever use it be sure to contact me and turn it in," Joseph said as Malik lifted the gun and felt its weight in his grip.

"Nice, huh?" asked Joseph.

Malik nodded, impressed. "Yeh," he breathed out, turning the six shot chamber, the hollow tips of cold bullets winking at him.

Chapter Twenty-Two

Intruders In The Dark

The Long Beach Majestic car show sparkled with gleaming low-riders on gold spoked rims. It was Michael's idea. Roxanne accepted the invitation. It would give them a chance to talk.

"A bitch really got to grind," she was saying to Michael as they admired a '57 Bel Air with its chrome underbelly exposed as if lifting one leg to piss.

"Because I'm loyal I got real lawyer's fees and bail," Roxanne said in a hushed tone. She was responding to his suggestion that she let him take Malik's spot. He'd basically asked her to make Malik go through him.

"I understand that," Michael said. "But we go farther if you let me double your movement. We can lock it up all the way to Georgia."

This sounded good to her except one thing. "But because I'm loyal, I can't give you the keys to something that was started by the man I'm fighting for," she said.

"So, what you doin' with Malik?" asked Michael.

She thought of Malik as a combination brother and son, but she wouldn't admit this to Michael. Instead she said, "I promised his grandfather that I would look out for him."

Michael looked at her coolly, perhaps calculating the reason for this oath.

"Is this why we shouldn't have fucked after all these years?" she asked, smiling just the same, her eyes sparkling behind Cazal gold-framed aviator lenses.

Michael smiled. "Well, I got your back. Remember that," he said. "Freeway is sneaky. He got niggas in his pocket that stay shady. Too many lions in the street. We gotta build alliances."

Roxanne thought of this for a beat. She wondered exactly how far his alliances reached. "I don't know about alliances. I got people that I fuck with and people I watch."

"Sometimes the people you watching really wanna fuck with you. Like I said, double your movement. You can run it."

"So, what am I giving up in return for this fabulous opportunity?" she asked with a note of sarcasm before greeting and air kissing a smiling female friend.

"Access to your connect," he said after the silk-wrapped bejeweled woman had walked off.

"Again, you want access to something that's not mine to share."

"Malik got access?" asked Michael.

Roxanne hardly thought of Malik as having access to her connect. He didn't represent a threat to her.

Michael nodded knowingly when she hesitated with her response. "Don't answer that," he said. "Obviously it ain't none of my business."

And he was right, she thought to herself. Maybe it was just some good fucking. And what was the problem with keeping it like that?

Roxanne was rescued from reminding him that she had other obligations by her ringing phone. They'd made their way to his candy purple dropped Silverado truck. The matching Flintstone canopy top poked out in spots like a tent.

"Hi, Malik," answered Roxanne, getting into the passenger seat. "How are you?"

"Good. Just stepped out from talking to Joseph. He wanna know how many he gotta buy to get to five each," said Malik.

That's just like having access to my connect, she thought to herself, ironically, looking to Michael as he weaved to the fast lane.

"Tell him I'll look into it," she said, reminding herself to ask Saul what it was that Joseph Mordecai really wanted.

"Okay. I'll slide to Pearl tomorrow."

Roxanne was surprised at his directness with making his schedule. She decided not to remind him that it was best to handle all transactions in a day.

"You got other plans for tonight?" she asked, hoping she sounded lighthearted enough.

"Yeh. I'm with a friend."

She wanted to ask if Shoota was with him, but resisted this. She swooned with innuendo. "A girl?" she asked.

"Yeh."

Roxanne wanted to know who this girl was. Where'd they meet? How? What about Trinity?

"Be careful," said Roxanne. "So, you'll be back definitely tomorrow then?"

"Prolly late though. I got some looking around to do," he said, not mentioning his meetings with two dudes who run separate projects.

"Okay. Well," she began, steeling herself against some emotion, which made her want to order him home. "Take it easy. See you soon," she added with masked heartbreak.

Michael gave her that cool stare again after she'd ended the call.

"What..." she said. "Don't get all touchy feely on me."

Michael chuckled.

"So, you gonna give me some dick and be of sound mind afterwards?" she asked.

"Oh, you got jokes," he said, chuckling. "Cascade Inn sound good? My granny home. I plan on you making a little noise."

"Oh, really," she said, laughing out. "Daddy got something to prove."

It wasn't until he was checked in and they were walking up the stairs to a corner suite that she remembered Freeway Rick owned the Cascade Inn. The room was in a corner off a short hallway, facing an ice machine.

"This place wouldn't have been my choice," she said, preparing to step ahead of him as he opened the door.

"You don't support black businesses?" he asked, following her through the door.

Roxanne was about to comment on Freeway Rick's black business approach, namely an ice machine in a far corner of the L-shaped two-story inn—most rooms facing the parking lot—when Michael was pushed into her.

Two men wearing all black rushed in behind Michael, large black guns pointed at them. Their eyes were squinted tight in the narrow holes of their black ski masks.

It happened swiftly. The large red muzzle flash beat the bang sound, forcing Roxanne's eyes closed. Brain matter splashed against her face before the second boom and flash of the other gun. Then all was silent and in slow motion. Through a haze of fright and blood she watched as the black ghosts rushed through the room, snatching open drawers and the closet.

She lay motionless, Michael's open brain before her, spilling large clumps of blood and brain tissue. She could feel them whoosh past her, the familiar jingle of the metal clasps of a large handbag with them.

Not until the door was slammed shut and the intruders gone did sound return. She blinked away the blood and heard the hissing and gurgling sound coming from Michael.

Chapter Twenty-Three

Friend Or Foe

And beside the heavy piece of steal that with just pulling it out dispersed the crowd, Joseph had given Malik $10,000 cash, more than he'd ever had of his own at one time.

Joseph appreciated Malik's cool style. He said that Malik was unassuming. And thanked him for delivering his product to him discreetly.

Malik remembered thinking of Shoota at the point, feeling validated in his decision to keep Shoota away.

And surprisingly, while coming down to the base of Lytle Creek, Elisa suggested, jokingly, that he might as well get an apartment in San Bernardino.

There was a quiet, elegant, four-unit complex near Lytle Creek. It was neat, reserved, and modern. Elisa said she knew the family that owned it. Friends of her father. They were Nigerian.

Malik never imagined that the manager would be so generous. The apartment looked like it should be in a magazine. It was black leather, white marble, and chrome everywhere.

Malik felt nothing when he dropped the $10,000 on the apartment for a six-month lease that Elisa had put in her name. It only seemed right to have a place of his own.

He'd been giving this some thought, only it had been with Trinity. She'd brought up the idea after announcing she was pregnant. He'd said to look for one. It was what he thought would be nice. Two girlfriends and two apartments.

Malik felt as if everything was going as it was supposed to be going. She was the one who suggested he not tell Shoota, already seeing things his way.

And they'd spent the night in their new apartment, furnished with the best of everything. And made slow love. In the place she'd be waiting for his return.

Malik could still feel her body twined with his as Shoota turned down a long drive, four story units ahead, spanning the length of a football field. The Meridians I. Apparently there was another complex like this one. Shoota said they'll go there next.

The low ceilinged apartments had small doors, most filled with the body of a woman, either with or without a child at their hip.

Shoota winded his way through the rows of appraising men, stopping once to ask for Victor.

"Me and Victor was in placement together," said Shoota. "He run these niggas."

Shoota drove deep into the projects, by trash bins and long rows of parking stalls. They reached an open courtyard surrounded by apartments. A small gathering of baggy clothed men turned their way.

"There that nigga go," said Shoota, pointing to a tall yellow man with a long jheri curl. He was dragging a contingent of the small gathering with him.

"Wassup, Shoota," said the yellow man, his thick neck hung with several gold rope necklaces; a diamond encrusted lion's head dangling from the fattest chain.

Shoota introduced Victor to Malik, saying how Malik was his boy. "He got the plug to save you money," added Shoota about Malik.

Victor smiled, his mouth perpetually wet like a kid who was always eating candy. "Oh, yeh," he said, looking at Malik slowly from toe to head. "How can you do that?" he asked.

"Ten a brick," said Shoota.

Victor shot a sharp look at Shoota. "Damn, nigga," he began, "can the nigga speak for his self?" Malik was surprised by Shoota's reaction. He'd never seen someone talk to him like this and get away with it.

"I might can get close to ten each, but it depend on how much you buy and how often," said Malik.

Victor nodded, smiling. "Gimme one for ten this first time," he said. "Come back next week and we'll talk about moving ten a week for closest you can get to ten each."

Malik could see the ambition in Victor's light brown eyes. They sparkled with opportunity. Malik saw how this place could be flooded with cocaine. The city was dry, Roxanne had said.

Malik looked to Shoota, his eyes hurt and hopeful, before replying, "Alright."

Victor's contingent, having heard the deal, looked at

Malik anew, having misjudged his plain dress.

Malik split the ten thousand with Shoota. This seemed to soothe his ego. There was one kilo left. And one more project apartment complex. This one identical to the first. Across the street and apparently controlled by a rival gang.

On the porch of the first apartment to the right were maybe ten young women, two getting their hair braided. On the lawn, near the curb were nearly fifty men. They were mostly all dressed in baggy designer matching jeans and jackets. Large gold Turkish ropes hung from their necks.

A few peeled from the group, all gripping large pistols, led by one who peered low, brushing thick dreads from his dark face. He raised one hand, easing the eager triggers beside him.

"Me and this nigga was in camp together. Nellis. He knocked a nurse up there. She gave me some pussy 'cuz he told her to." Shoota introduced him as Jamaica Rob.

Malik shook his chiseled, leather hand. "Malik Toole," he said, holding Rob's steady gaze.

Rob grinned, his young teeth framed in gold. Where Victor was a player type, this grimy dude was from the dirt.

"Rude boy," Rob said, looking to Shoota. "This him you tell rasta 'bout?" he said, pulling a shiny stick of cherry root from his thick lips.

Shoota grinned. "Yeh. This my boy," he replied.

"Rude here say you got chickens all day for lesser," said Rob, looking to Malik.

"Yeh," began Malik, looking across the men behind Rob, some looking off, passing a large joint between themselves, "I got a little work to get off. And a steady plug."

Rob shot his head up, moving thick branches of hair from his eye. "What's the lesser?" he asked, looking to Shoota casually, asking, "You met him to Victor?"

Shoota hesitated.

"Yeh," said Malik. "It's all good. His business ain't your business. Your business ain't his business."

Shoota started to say something until Rob began laughing. Then he shook his head up and down.

"Malik," he said, reaching up to grab Malik's shoulder, steering him towards the apartment where the ladies were braiding hair.

"Rude boy no pussy," said Rob to Malik, then waving over the girls he said, "All dem queens ride. Sisters, cousins, girlfriends." The ladies hissed at him, some casting appraising eyes to Malik, others asking what his name was.

"I tell it when it need knowin!" Rob said from inside the apartment, Malik following closely. The smell of Curry fried chicken dominated the room. A small group of children poked their heads around the edge of a hallway.

A tall, shapely woman in a tube dress emerged from the door, across a living room of brown suede couches and glass tables. "What you bring here?" she asked, holding a large dripping fork over a napkin.

Rob sneaked up on her and kissed her hot cheek before he said, "Malik Toole, Ma!" Throwing his jeweled hand to Malik as if he were a game show prize.

She stopped to consider if she should know the name. She looked to Malik as if for familiar features of a relative.

"Why not to your own house?" she said, turning back to the kitchen with a giant swaying of hips and ass. Rob waved him through, by peeking kids, and through a narrow hallway.

Malik suspected this was his childhood room. He obviously had his own apartment. Malik noticed for the first time that Shoota hadn't followed. He wondered if he even made it inside the house.

Rob gestured to a twin bed on the wall, facing the wall he was lounging on. The walls were adorned with a growing Jamaica Rob, in sports gear for soccer and football. Quarterback. His teams and later familiar faces surrounded him at lavish picnic functions and parties.

"What's the lesser, bruddah?" asked Rob, his dreads dropping across his body as he leaned on one elbow.

"What you tryna spend?" replied Malik.

"I spend double if I the only one," Rob said this with a flattening grin.

Malik was reminded of his grandfather by the steady cool of Rob's eyes.

"Everybody eat less blood in the street," said Malik.

Rob sat up, his gold swinging with him. He cocked his head for a second. "Give me what you give the pretty boy," Rob said.

"This what I'll do," began Malik. "I got one right now I'll give you for ten. Each one you want after that is fifteen."

Rob's brow furrowed before he nodded with some new understanding. He stood, rocking and smiling as he extended his hand to Malik.

"Rude mahn got dat plug," sang Rob, his grip firm in Malik's hand.

Jamaica Rob knelt to the bed he'd jumped from and pulled out a shoebox. Then another. He opened them both. He pulled up bundle after bundle of money, some tied with shoe strings, none the same size.

Rob showed Malik a fat roll of one hundred dollar bills. "Dat ten," he said. "How many you want?" he asked, chuckling, pulling open more boxes, all stocked with cash bundles.

"I got a money counter," Malik said, remembering that Joseph said he'd need it. The big gun was tucked safely under his leather coat, the way he imagined Joseph Mordecai wore his.

"You not staying to eat?" said the lady in the tube dress,

knowing her now, from the pictures, as Rob's mother.

Malik imagined eating some of that good smelling Curry chicken, counting money, and chilling with Rob. He'd show Rob his mobile phone. Call Trinity and Elisa. Check on his mom.

Malik looked to Rob, whose head nodded slightly. "Mind if I eat in Rob's room?" asked Malik, liking the way her pretty brown face broke into a smile. He felt her approval swim over him and to the other women in the room and the children peeking from the hallway.

Rob pushed by Malik, whispering with warning eyes, "You dunnit, rude mahn. She treat you like her son now." He smiled with this, turning to his mother. "In my room, Ma," he said with a wide grin.

Chapter Twenty-Four

Fading Memories

Boom. Blam.

That was all Roxanne remembered. She couldn't offer more. She couldn't hear out of her left ear. She couldn't rightly remember how many sets of pigs in uniforms and suits had asked her the same thing: "Did you hear them speak?" *No,* she'd responded in every case. *All I heard was, Boom! Blam!*

They'd tired of writing every question on a notepad. First the uniforms, asking if she knew of anything the robbers may have been after. Of course they asked if she had any enemies.

Apparently there wasn't much police could do when two people follow a couple into a motel owned by a drug dealer, kill a gang member from Watts, and deafen the wife of Tootie Reese, himself a cop killer.

When the two ebony and ivory federal officers arrived, after having last seen her at the shop—wanting her to become a snitch—she'd mastered the art of being totally deaf. The doctor said that she could hear on her left. She heard the white pig say word was that it was a mistaken identity, but watched as he wrote it all down and lifted it to her eyes.

"But of course that changes if they took something," white fed pig said.

"Gotta write it," black fed pig reminded him, lounging lazily against the hospital door, moving his shoulder every time a nurse walked in or out.

"Naw," said white fed pig, searching Roxanne's drugged eyes. "She's playing possum. She knows more than what she's letting on."

Roxanne remembered the tap of their feet. The time away inside. Then them running back with the jingling sounds of metal clasps.

"It's her bed. We invited her in," said black fed pig, being suddenly shoved aside.

"Everybody out!" shouted Saul, his small round stomach pushing into the room, his face flush. His briefcase swung in his grip as if it were empty.

Saul rushed to the side of the bed. "Don't say a word," he said, looking at the thick bandage that covered half her head. He suddenly looked to the pigs. "Out!" he shouted, his arms thrusting towards the door, ushering them through. He looked more impressive behind his desk or in a courtroom. Roxanne wanted to laugh, but resisted this. The room was empty except for the beeping of the monitors and Saul's heavy breathing.

"You need a doctor?" she asked after he'd pulled up a chair by her bedside.

"No, I'm okay," he breathed out, lapping at his dry lips. "What the hell happened?" he asked hoarsely.

"I really don't know," replied Roxanne. "It all happened so quick."

"Think you might have been followed?"

"It's possible," she whispered.

"Well, good thing you aren't dead," he said. "You don't think they were after you?"

She'd never considered this. She considered that Michael had an enemy she knew nothing about. She also considered that it may have been Hill, thinking Michael was Shoota. Or what if it was Hill and wanted Michael anyway? And left her alive to collect on Shoota.

"What?" asked Saul, looking at Roxanne's wide, thinking eyes. "You know something? "

It was the tone of his voice that made him sound guilty. If not for this, then for something else he had his hand in. At more than any other time she didn't trust Saul.

"Naw," she said, recovering from her realization. "I don't know. They could have bin tryna kill me. I was in front of Michael," she said, but this didn't explain what they left with.

Roxanne wondered if Shoota was with Malik. She doubted this could have been him. She moaned, suddenly realizing that no one had told her if Michael was alive or not. She suspected that he was dead. The image of his exploding head played on a loop in her mind. Saul tapped her arm lightly, absorbed in his own thoughts.

"Get me my phone, Saul, please. And call in the doctor for me," she said, lifting from a shallow bed of sorrow.

Roxanne looked to the window, the moon high in the night sky, Malik darting across her thoughts like a quick thief of time.

Chapter Twenty-Five

I Got Yo' Back

All Shoota knew was that Malik and Elisa went to a motel. He still had no idea that Malik had leased a fully furnished apartment at the base of Lytle Creek, a small cul-de-sac of four unit apartments, occupied mostly during the snow season.

Malik now understood the fine furnishings. A six-month lease was perfect. Elisa was waiting for him when he brought in the last of the groceries. While he was touring the projects she was buying towels, utensils, and bed linen.

"Home away from home," said Elisa from the spacious

kitchen, stocking it with the ingredients of a vegetarian cabbage dish she planned to make. Malik wished his mother could see this place. She would like it, he thought to himself.

"I'll sleep at Jennifer's when you're away," she said, her eyes betraying all the unasked questions. "I ordered a phone in case you need me and I'm here."

"That's cool," replied Malik, handing her two large cranberry juice drinks. "The camp not far away. I'll be up here regular," he added, thinking this would work just fine, as long as Trinity didn't find out.

"It's perfect, right?" she said, rushing to him and leaning on tiptoe to kiss his lips.

"A private spot is just what I need," he said, grabbing her tight ass beneath a soft dress. "And a woman I can trust."

"I got your back," she said softly, wrapping her hands around the back of his neck. "Whatever we do, let's do it one hundred percent. Let me help you and be someone you can count on." Malik looked into her deep black eyes. He'd never known a woman like Elisa. Confident. Natural. Focused. Rich.

"I wanna be somebody you can count on, too. I like who you are," he responded, pulling her to him, kissing her tenderly.

She'd lit scented candles. The master bedroom was dominated by a high, big bed with thick wooden posts at its ends. The large open closet space already held several hundred thousand dollars in cash. The dark wood end table was covered with stacks and tied rolls of money he'd pulled from his pockets, a paper bag from Victor, and a shoebox from Jamaica Rob.

The thing he wanted Elisa to see was the shoebox filled with baby Christmas trees of marijuana with orange and purple hairs.

"Yeh," she giggled out, lifting a fat bud of herb from the shoebox. "This is nice," she added. There was nothing like laying back on a plush bed with a pretty girl, smoking bud, money in your pocket...

Elisa's gentle nudge broke him from these thoughts. The overhead ceiling fan could be hypnotizing. She passed him the joint, her dark skin an inviting gleam through the swift plume of smoke.

Her pussy was soft to the touch, lightly covered with a soft dew of silken hairs. He rubbed it softly, taking a pull off the joint.

"There's a safe behind that picture," she said, pointing to a portrait of French General, Alexandre Dumas, sitting high on a reeling white horse, his sword held up.

"Serious," he said, glad to hear this. "This spot get more and more fancy."

"Yeh, now lay back," she said, raising up and lifting his boxers from his body. Elisa took his flaccid joint in her mouth. She sucked, it grew in pulses on her tongue. Her tapered fingers dragged along his muscled stomach. He was now hard in her mouth, straining at the corners of her lips.

Malik enjoyed the way her thick dark hair fanned down around her face, resting on his thighs, tickling him with soft strokes while she went up and down around the head of his swollen dick.

He maneuvered her around, the plump ass in his grip, the soft muff at his lips. She smelled of some dark flower, intoxicating. He tasted her, kissed her, and sucked at the tender lips, licking firm flesh between his lips.

Her ass grinded back, rotated on his tongue, and took it inside to explore. Her mouth popped off his dick with mild suctioning.

Elisa dragged her wet pussy down the length of his body before fitting his dick inside of her. She grabbed his ankles, bent forward, and grinded up and down on his downward straining dick. Malik braced against the odd angle and the pleasure. Her ass rolled and slid in his grip, bending and stroking him inside her pussy.

Elisa found her way around to him, turning on his dick, now kissing him as she slid along his body. "We are great together, aren't we?" she whispered, nibbling on his ear. Malik bit her on the shoulder softly in response.

"We met for a purpose," she added, kissing him along his neck. "Will we deny its purpose?"

Malik absorbed her stabbing down on his dick, pushing him deep inside her. He couldn't deny its purpose, swelling, growing hotter inside her to prove the point.

Chapter Twenty-Six

From Boy To Man

Roxanne had always hated hospitals. She'd seen enough death in those beds to become a skeptic as to the benefits of a doctor's care. All these tests. Trying to find out if there were side effects to the trauma, treatment, or recovery. And then there were the blood tests, eye exam, and reflexology tests. All to prove she had good balance and could see full pictures. Apparently, the hearing loss would improve. Maybe in a year she'd have full hearing back, but never like before, so the doctor said.

"Yes, baby," she said into the portable phone. "I'll be

there in a minute. We'll go to breakfast," she promised her son. The heavy bandage had been replaced by a simple earplug of gauze to control leaking. Her ear was filled with medicine to repair the eardrum.

Roxanne had become a minor celebrity within the ward. The nurses looked at her with a bit of awe. She'd reputed to be a female cocaine dealer, whose husband was shot dead in front of her. Bolstering this rumor was the ever present police detail outside her front door. And the early visits by the suited DEA detectives.

Cocaine was changing the kind of people who ended up in the ER. They now had portable phones, dressed nicely, and were soon visited by police and lawyers. The nurses were thankful that a posse of thuggish men hadn't arrived to congest the lobby. Or worse, that a shoot hadn't erupted.

It was in the spirit of this thankfulness, mystery, and respect that Roxanne was released from the hospital. There was one person she'd called to come get her.

Malik entered the room a changed man, right before her eyes. "This place gives me the shakes," he said, not having to mention this was the hospital where his grandfather passed away.

Roxanne's eyes couldn't take him all in. His face gleamed with accomplishment. Gone was the boy trying to figure it out. Standing before her was a man who realized his self worth, and growing.

"Well, don't you look like a college man," said Roxanne, smiling at him openly, liking the button up collar shirt and Sperry Top Sider boat shoes. "Who dressing you?" she said, nearly jealous as she stepped by him into the hallway.

Malik resisted telling her that Elisa stocked the closet with new clothes for him. She'd even stocked the bathroom with anything he might need, including mouthwash.

"Just did a little shopping," he said, waiting for the

nurse, standing by with a wheelchair to insist Roxanne used it. It was hospital policy.

"Thanks for coming to get me. I can't believe what happened," complained Roxanne as they rode down in the elevator.

Malik held his tongue, aware of the attentive nurse riding with them. He wheeled her through the early morning lobby of scheduled appointments and into the bright rising sun.

"Oh, my gawd," hissed Roxanne, squinting to the sun.

"Am I taking you to your house?" he asked, watching as she pulled a pair of Cazal shades from her purse. They didn't look so impressive now.

"Sure," replied Roxanne. "You've never been to my house, huh?" she said absently as they reached the car.

Malik handed the wheelchair off to the nurse and got behind the wheel. Finally alone he turned to her. "What's going on?" he asked directly.

Roxanne explained the entire evening, beginning from when they'd left the car show. She explained that her and Michael went back to high school. She didn't share that she believed he was robbed. And nothing about thinking it may have been Hill, mistaking Michael for Shoota. But that didn't seem right.

"You take Shoota with you?" she asked.

"Yeh," replied Malik, satisfied with Shoota's presence. He'd learned a lot about Shoota and met a solid friend in Jamaica Rob.

"He plugged me with a cat name Victor," he said. "From the Meridian projects," he added. Rob had never questioned him about who he was plugged with. He recognized it and received it. Nothing more.

Malik moved now with having learned the next level of the game. Where people aren't valued in money, but in access and friendship. Where a beautiful woman from a rich family chose a young drug courier and raised his game.

"Victor," repeated Roxanne, as if searching for the name.

Malik wondered if her sighing was from the pain or the name. It was with this exchange he'd confirmed in his decision to keep the apartment and Elisa to himself.

"Yeh. He good for one a week at that price."

Roxanne nodded. "That's good money, huh?" she said.

It was more than Malik ever thought he would make. But he had seen more. He had seen the possibilities.

He was now in a place where millions of dollars were at his reach. Where young men his age were moving in silence and violence.

"Sure, that's good money," he said, deciding to keep Joseph Mordecai to himself. "It's wide open out there. If I could promise a lower price for each brick over five we might do some damage," he added.

Roxanne cocked her head. "What you know that I don't?" she asked. "Like, how much you tryna move?"

"I got a few people looking twenty, ten, five and on. I need to have room to offer deals."

Roxanne considered this. If there was one person she needed, it was Malik. His grandfather had told her enough about him to know he was loyal, but would require appreciation. In her gut she felt the pull. First, Saul suggesting she give Malik the keys.

"So, how're things with Joseph Mordecai? Saul says he seems to be big on you," she said.

"Cool. He just happy to get good prices. He got some cool spots where he be chillin at," he added, neglecting to mention the pistol and money counter Joseph had given him.

And it was more of a left hand right hand thing. Elisa had it. Jamaica Rob had it. They didn't question what was in the other hand. And there was Joseph, looking to make everyone's hands better. In style even.

"Saul thinks I should fall back," said Roxanne, leaning into the seat, facing Malik. "Left on Wilcox," she added, directing traffic going towards Wilshire on Western.

"Oh, yeh?" said Malik, thinking that would fall right into what Joseph Mordecai wanted. The direct plug.

"He thinks you're grown enough to handle it," she said, looking at him carefully, familiar sights of home passing by with the sway of tall palm trees.

This could solve everything, Malik thought to himself. "I can do what you need me to do. Leave the rest to me. It's going to be more than enough for everybody."

She was privately impressed. A huge weight was lifted from her shoulders. He was so innocent, she thought to herself, yet so capable.

"Right here," she said, directing him to a large two-story house set far back from the curb. All the houses were set far back.

"What they call this, a mini mansion?" asked Malik, pulling into a winding driveway behind a black grill security gate.

"My husband bought it," she said.

Malik pretended not to know the details about her husband, as if Shoota had never shared them.

"So, you basically want a price you can deal down to?" she asked, turning to him, thinking this could neutralize any of those pulls she was feeling.

"Yeh. Your minimum," he began, throwing his arm over the seat back and turning to her. "I'ma always be loyal to you. You're family."

Roxanne smiled, feeling reassured. "Eight thousand. Anything over that is yours," she said.

Malik calculated that he'd get two thousand for each

kilo sold to Joseph Mordecai, who got each one for ten thousand, buying twenty at a time. "That's good money," he said, nodding. Never mind that she was the center of a federal investigation, recent victim of a violent crime.

Malik felt protected from this mayhem. He kept Jamaica Rob to himself. Eating Curry chicken while the money counter had bleeped and blurred money, they'd smoked and shared stories of playing in some of the same basketball tournaments. Jamaica Rob had played in all the semi-pro tournaments Malik hoped to one day play.

Malik thought of Jamaica Rob and his friends and family as a private army. He felt good knowing he could give Rob a good deal. Make the family grow.

He thought of Elisa, money pouring over her head. Her beautiful black hair tossing and her laughing with money falling onto their bed. And Trinity. She wanted a beauty salon with booths for manicures and pedicures. Something fancy. It was as if she'd anticipated his eventual rise in the drug game.

Roxanne smiled. "I'll let Mario know you'll be calling him direct. I'll simply let you know who and at what price to drop and add that to yours."

"I get everything over eight with yours too?"

"Of course," she replied quickly.

Malik felt his muscles flex and turn hot. "That's good eatin'," said Malik. "As my grandfather would say."

Malik resolved himself to keep his money a secret. He thanked Elisa for her thoughtfulness. A safe was perfect. It only seemed right now that he had an apartment. A safe place with a beautiful and smart woman to share it with. A place that no one knew about.

Chapter Twenty-Seven

These Niggas Ain't Loyal

Shoota had been remarkably silent, Malik thought to himself, turning the corner onto his block. He'd dropped Shoota off earlier, before dropping off the money at the stash house and going to pick up Roxanne. His mom had been gone. Trinity was at the nail shop. And here was Shoota, stepping from the curb.

"What it do?" asked Malik, stopping in the middle of the street.

Shoota leaned to the window. "You dropped me off to go see that bitch, huh?" said Shoota.

The trip to San Bernardino had helped Malik see Shoota in a new light. On a bigger stage.

"What's up though," replied Malik, safe in the knowledge that he was more respected than Shoota by his folks.

"We can run that shit out there," sneered Shoota. "My niggas feel you," he added.

Malik didn't remember Shoota ever making his way to the bedroom after grabbing the money counter.

Left hand, right hand. Malik decided to keep his new deal with Roxanne private. So, it was to Malik's surprise when Shoota said that Hill wanted to rob Roxanne.

"What?" asked Malik, not sure he heard correct, already parked in the street too long.

"And the nigga want me to go with him," said Shoota, looking to Malik as if awaiting permission.

"What they gon' rob?" asked Malik.

Shoota looked off down the street before he turned back to Malik. "The stash house," he said.

Malik struggled to conceal his disbelief. He decided to treat it as normal conversation. "So, what you telling me for?"

Shoota grinned. "Nigga. So we know it's there."

Malik calmed himself. He looked off, then to his childhood friend. "If I wanted to rob her I wouldn't need Hill to do it."

Shoota got excited. "Me and you, my nigga. Let's get her. We can act like a nigga tied you up. Just keep the door open and I'll creep up in there."

Malik grinned. "I wouldn't need you either if I wanted to get her," said Malik, ashamed for his friend. He was sad that Shoota couldn't come with him to where he was going.

"What you care about that bitch for my nigga. Bitch threw us some crumbs. I didn't even have to roll to know she clocking at least half a million."

JOY DEJA KING & PETER MACK

There it was, Malik thought to himself. Shoota felt shut out. He'd rather destroy everything and take for himself what he could.

Malik saw the disloyalty and deceit in his broken soul. This was how his grandfather referred to people like Shoota. Broken souls.

"Talk to me my nigga," said Malik. "This is our thang. Anything that goes on in our thang is our business. Leave them outsiders out," said Malik, bringing Shoota closer so he could catch him better.

Shoota nodded, rubbing his chin, liking the sound of that.

"I bet you got more money in your pocket than they do," said Malik, adding, "They could be tryna set you up."

Shoota had never considered this. "Them niggas prolly the ones did that shit to her dude from Watts."

Malik shook his head, remembering that Roxanne had asked where Shoota was. She'd suspected it could have been Shoota.

"You think it could be a set up?" asked Shoota.

"It don't matter if we stick together," said Malik.

Shoota smiled. "You my boy. I'ma keep it real with you, but that bitch ain't nothing to me."

Malik was exhausted. He didn't want to remind Shoota how she'd put money in his pocket.

"Leave my shit alone," said Malik, extending his hand. "You with me or not?" he wanted to know.

Shoota nodded and gripped his hand. "You right. I'm with you."

Malik considered throwing him some work to put him in traffic so the streets could have its way with him, but cooled on that idea. To have him close enough to watch was good enough.

"I still ain't seen Mom and my girl. They was gone

when I dropped you off earlier," said Malik. "Let me get down there."

Pulling away he decided he'd leave Shoota in L.A. when he went back to San Bernardino. Let the streets feed his hunger.

Dutch was standing in front of his '65 Chevy Impala SS. The black candy paint gleamed under the moonlight. He smiled when Malik pulled the stock yellow Chevy Nova to the curb.

Malik watched as he fastened chrome snaps along the car, locking the black canvas top in place.

"I'm digging your college fit," said Dutch, his fat gold rope shimmering under the yellow cast of the streetlamp at the corner.

Malik stopped at the curb, carrying the portable phone and grapefruit juice Trinity said she'd wanted. And she said that his mother hadn't come out her room since earlier.

"What it do, playa?" said Dutch, rubbing his palms apart, the diamond-encrusted gold watch on his wrist sparkling.

"Waddup, Dutch," said Malik, looking to Dutch's Chevy. "How much can I get one those for?"

Dutch looked back at the Chevy quickly before turning to Malik. "You can have that one for four thousand dollars," he said.

Malik believed him. It sounded like a deal. The chrome Dayton 100 spoke rims wrapped in small buff shiny tires were seductive. Malik thought it would look good at the apartment with Elisa.

"I'll buy it from you," he said. "It'll be next week though."

Dutch held his palms up. "Ain't no sign on it," he said.

"Yeh. I ain't gon' drive it around here though. I'm taking it to basketball camp with me." Malik nodded with this new idea, liking it.

"That sounds good," Dutch said. "Look like you getting your weight up."

"Yeh. I got a little something goin' on. What you tryna do?" asked Malik, eager to be able to offer Dutch a good deal.

"If you can get me a few of them bricks for thirty, powder, that would be solid." Malik marveled that the prices were inflated that even the discount left decent profit.

"I can get three for thirty for you," Malik said, inhaling slowly, the smell of the city dropping on him.

"You taking the car for four?"

Malik considered this. "Yeh, but I probably won't move the car 'til next week. I'll have that three within a couple of days." Malik imagined that Dutch was probably buying two kilos for thirty.

"Solid," said Dutch. "I'll hold it for you. If you want to move it with a flatbed let me know."

Malik had thought to drive it himself. "I might do that," he said.

Malik missed seeing his grandfather's Lincoln Continental in the driveway. He was reminded that he wouldn't be sitting in his favorite chair, watching a western movie, and eating roasted peanuts.

"Who bought that for you?" asked Trinity, neglecting to say hello, when Malik stepped through the front door.

"One of my connects be shipping clothes. Square shit like this," he said, dismissing her suspicion.

"You look nice," she responded, wrapping her arms around his waist.

Malik enjoyed her hug and playful rub across his dick. "Missed you, baby," he said, kissing her on the lips. "How's Mom?" he asked.

"She won't answer the door. I asked if she was hungry, she said no."

Malik followed Trinity into the bedroom. "How long

she been in there?"

"I got here at one. She came in at two and went to her room," said Trinity.

"How'd she look when you saw her?"

Trinity sat on the bed. "I was in here. She just passed by. That's when I asked if she was hungry."

"And she bin in her room ever since?" asked Malik. He'd been hoping she would get back to her normal self after the funeral.

Trinity nodded. "Go check on her," she said, laying back on the bed.

Malik was afraid. Afraid for his mother. Her bedroom door was closed. He wondered if she'd been going to work. And where was she this morning?

He knocked. "Mama... Ma!"

Malik opened the door. His mother's small body lay amidst heaps of clothes. On the corner chair, long dresser, and hanging on every doorknob or lampshade were clothes, towels, scarves, and blouses. The room smelled of competing perfumes. Malik found his mother's head and brushed away the hair from her face. Her eyes were closed. Her skin was soft.

"Mama," whispered Malik, stroking the hair across her neck.

She was warm. She smiled, rolling her face against his touch. "I'm okay," she whispered. "Just need to rest awhile."

"You feel okay, Ma?"

"Congratulations on your new baby," she said low. "She got you now."

Malik remembered all those conversations about making sure not to get her pregnant before he made it to the NBA.

"I want someone different for you," she'd said. "Somebody from a nice family. With a good heart."

Though she had said it jokingly, as if it being impossible to make those odds so why not wish it.

Malik smiled now, thinking of Elisa. He wanted to tell her about Elisa, but it didn't feel like the right time. He wanted to say how Trinity and Elisa both come from good families and they both have good hearts, yet they are as different as night and day. And he couldn't give up either one.

He wondered what her reaction would be if he said that he would be a millionaire by the time basketball camp was over. He wondered what that would mean for her. But this was better left unsaid. All in due time.

"You just take it easy," he said, his hand rubbing along her back. "I got it."

"You be careful," she said. "Stay true to who you are. And family."

"Always, Mama. Always," Malik assured her.

Malik saw family in a new way. It reached further. It consisted of people who shared the same vision. Shared vision was everything.

Trinity was nearly asleep when Malik crept into the bedroom. He'd sat with his mother until the late night, sharing stories about his grandfather. Like the time his grandfather pulled a shotgun on a burglar. He held the man at gunpoint until the police arrived. Trinity's body was warm under the covers; in a t-shirt and panties. Malik snuggled close to her neck. "Marvellus Toole the second," he whispered, his face close to hers.

She smiled. She had thought of naming their child after his grandfather, no matter if she were girl or boy. "I was gonna do that anyway," she said. "Because I know you're not selfish."

Malik agreed, liking that she knew him so well. "We gon' be straight," he said. "Wanna get an apartment?"

"Your mom coming?"

"Naw. If she want to, but she might stay here," replied Malik, waiting for Trinity's happiness at the idea.

Trinity turned to her back and looked up to Malik in the dim light. "How deep are you?" she asked.

"Deeper," he responded. "But a better deeper." He kissed her in the darkness.

"Better, huh," she said, playfully punching his ribs. "Well, I want a car."

"You go it," he said.

"Shopping?" she asked. "I am pregnant, after all."

"You got it." He kissed her softly on the lips.

"I wanna stay here for now. With your mother," she said at last, rubbing her fingers across his stomach.

"You always right, baby," Malik sang in her ear before nibbling on it.

They collapsed onto each other in soft laughter, Malik shedding his clothes and finding himself naked under the covers with her. She warmed him with her body as they moved together.

Chapter Twenty-Eight

Pieces Of The Puzzle

Roxanne refused to be afraid. She was unapologetic when showing up at Maximum Roxy's. Nisha was even surprised to see her. The rumors had been swirling. One rumor had it that she had been set up by Michael, but it all went wrong somehow. Nisha told this rumor with the odd head nod, as if asking Roxanne to please deny this.

Roxanne only shook her head. "You got anything better?" asked Roxanne as Nisha set up her work station.

"Girl, I ain't gonna lie," began Nisha, one jeweled hand coming to her breast. "If we wasn't girls I woulda bin left."

Roxanne laughed this off.

"Serious," continued Nisha. "Bitches getting robbed and here next you nearly got killed."

"I wanna leave me," said Roxanne. "Trust me."

"But that shit is crazy, right?" said Nisha, looking for an explanation.

"What can I tell you," replied Roxanne, taking a step towards her office. "I just saw a crazy car accident on the freeway over here." She shrugged. "Proves you never know." Roxanne exhaled mightily once in her office. She checked her hand to see if it was shaking. It was not. She took a much easier breath, sitting at the desk.

Roxanne missed Malik. Since she'd given him personal access to Mario she had to be patient to get new information. Malik had a habit of waiting until the last hour of the day to confirm his movements. They hardly spent time together anymore. She resisted the urge to call him, feeling jealous when he was unavailable or was busy while talking to her. She struggled with the fact that now most people were seeing what she saw in him. He was a natural hustler with charm and finesse.

Roxanne busied herself with accounting duties and a quick call from Saul. He wanted to know how close she was to having one million dollars in cash. Roxanne bristled at the way he questioned her with a note of doubt. She had never felt she couldn't trust Saul. She didn't feel trust in him now. She could feel him trying to see if she was afraid. She was satisfied with her decision to rely on Malik more in exchange for more money for him. She realized that there weren't many people she could trust. Malik was one of them. Hill walked through the front door after Nisha's first customer. Malik called just as she ended her call with Saul.

"I'm getting fifty-five," he said.

Roxanne calculated that twenty were for her clients.

She was impressed that he was moving an impressive amount of work. "Sounds good," she replied. "I'll be at Michael's funeral in an hour."

"Awright. I got you." Roxanne wanted to hear that he hoped to see her before he left. She wanted to talk to him about what happened to her. How she thought it could have been Shoota. She wanted to ask how things were with Shoota. And if they were together much. But she let the call end without bringing any of this up. He seemed so private, she thought to herself, eyeing Hill through the one-way mirror. Chills ran through her as she thought it could have easily been Hill who killed Michael.

She attempted a brave demeanor when she stepped from the office. She felt protected in designer jeans and black suede jockey boots. Hill suddenly looked like a rare yellow snake. This man she'd never seen before.

"What's hood, Rox," said Hill, strolling bow-legged to her. She was reminded of what Malik's grandfather told her one time. A snake also smiles, right before he bites you.

"Hey, what's good?" she replied, subtly replacing his hood with what a gangsta would say: 'good'; neighborhood Crips say, 'hood'.

Hill sneered. "We close," he said.

"You mean you tried already?" she asked, stepping to his side, looking out to his now gold Cadillac. It was black only days before.

"Hypothetically, we close," he said, turning towards the door. "Have my product for me," he added, sneering at the door.

Roxanne believed more than ever that Hill may be the one who shot the gun near her head. She wondered if he'd meant to miss. Maybe it was that other yellow snake, his brother Al, who killed Michael.

"You and Al are usually together," she observed,

walking casually towards him. "Is he okay?"

"Yeh. He hood," replied Hill, turning from her.

Roxanne watched him. His walk. It was an unusual walk. Like a cowboy. It all happened so fast. Two quick bangs. And then she couldn't hear. Blood was all over her face and in her hair. Michael's brain spilled out in chunks.

Hill didn't look at her until he was behind the wheel of the Cadillac, its tail jacked up like a scorpion's poisoned needle. He had the murderer's twinkle in his black eyes.

Roxanne closed the door as Hill turned from the lot, exhaling slowly, having no doubt that he would kill Shoota. She also now wondered how was it that someone could go up in Freeway Rick's hotel and kill somebody. Maybe Hill was Freeway's private killer. Maybe Freeway wanted Michael dead.

Roxanne collapsed on her office chair, the pieces of the puzzle settling before her. It made perfect sense. She looked to Nisha talking to her client, thinking that maybe she'd be better off with Shoota around. Give him damn near same deal as Malik. Flood the whole city. Fuck it.

But how can I warn him? she asked herself. The answer didn't come to her until she was parking at Forest Lawn cemetery. From her parking space she could see the big crowd of black people. They had the familiar stance and lean of proper people and gangsters. It was Michael's funeral.

Have Malik do it, she thought to herself. Tell Malik to warn him about a plot she overheard. She would suggest to Malik extending Shoota a fair deal to work with in L.A. She decided to offer Malik a better deal. Seven thousand per kilo. She still made two off each one.

Two birds with one stone, she thought to herself. She needed to make sure she saw Malik before he left for San Bernardino with fifty-five kilos of powder cocaine, when a familiar voice called her name. Freeway Rick.

"Maximum Roxy," he said, smiling, his red-tinted jheri curl glinting in the sunlight. "Strange times," he added.

"Strange indeed, Ricky," she replied. "How people can come up in your spot waving guns and killing people."

Freeway Rick shrugged. "Same way they run up in yo' spot and take purses and shit," he said, stepping away from her. "We both need security," he added over his shoulder.

Chapter Twenty-Nine

More Lies

Malik doubted that Shoota really wanted to go with him. He was tempted to offer him a kilo on consignment, sure that he'd get the money, if he survived long enough, but decided against this. He felt the need to have Shoota close, away from Hill, going against his earlier decision to leave him in L.A.

When Malik asked about him wanting to see Jennifer, Shoota responded he'd seen her enough already. And there was no explanation as to why not going to see Victor and Jamaica Rob. Malik agreed to ride alone, deciding to see

Roxanne, for sure, before he left. She needed to know what Hill was plotting.

Mario's Auto Repair looked closed to the casual observer. It was never opened after dark. This was Mario's idea. He liked to switch things up. Malik didn't mind. It felt like their own private arrangement now, especially since he was the one planning when and how much to pick up.

"*Buenas noches*," greeted Mario, pulling open the tall black gate. The evening traffic was light on Vernon Avenue, all the businesses closed.

Malik pulled to an empty spot to the now familiar red Chevy Nova. Black. Red. Yellow. They've all become his cars, each having its own personality. The red one had a bigger motor. It felt like a racecar.

"Mario. My friend," replied Malik, stepping from the yellow Nova and accepting the keys to the red one. "Here you go," he added, handing Mario four hundred and forty thousand dollars in a soft leather satchel.

Like a thief in the night, Malik emerged onto the dark streets with a car trunk full of powder cocaine. This red car had been outfitted with a special door compartment for the gift from Joseph. Malik had simply to show Mario the .44 Magnum.

He'd suggested tinted windows, but Mario shook his head. "Clean," he'd said.

Malik just doesn't like people seeing him on the phone. He stuck to back streets and freeways when he needed to make a call.

"How's Mama?" he asked Trinity, the phone discreetly to his ear.

"She's fine. She needed that little bit of time y'all shared. I think I'll rent a movie or something."

"Cool."

"She just stressing a little bit. I miss G'Pa too," said

Trinity.

"Yeh," responded Malik, never thinking someone could miss him as much as she did. "I'ma take both y'all shopping when I get back. And get you a car."

"Okay, baby," responded Trinity, the sadness of the conversation dampening his news. "You coming by before you leave?"

I just left there, he wanted to say, but instead said, "It's gon' be late and I'ma be dirty."

"Oh, yeh," she said low. "Be careful. I love you."

Malik ended the call feeling saddened as he turned onto a quiet street. The stash house was in the middle of the block. He passed a gold Cadillac, parked at the corner, behind a large truck. He would have paid more attention had it been black.

"Good evening," said Malik, loving the always cheerful voice of Elisa. He pulled to the back of the driveway and out of sight.

"Good evening, brother," she responded sexily. "I can't wait to see you."

Malik grinned, wanting to be in the apartment with her. "I'm on my way."

"Call when you get thirty minutes away so I can start dinner."

"Sounds like a plan," replied Malik. "I wish I was there to watch."

"Want me to wait," she teased. "I'll wear something sexy."

Malik chuckled. "Naw. Don't wait. But you can still wear something sexy," he said.

"So, you saying what I normally wear isn't sexy?" After a brief silence, she laughed. "I'm just playing," she said.

"You play too much." He smiled, having been caught off guard.

Her laughter was a musical note, floating in the air even after the call ended. Just as he was about to step through the back door of the house his portable phone rang.

"Hi," said Roxanne, her voice hurried. "You left yet?"

"Naw. I just got to the house," he replied, spotting the moon through the tall trees in the backyard.

"Good. I'm on my way. I need to talk to you."

"Yeh. I need to see you, too," he said, glad that she called to remind him. He was already thinking of the ride to Elisa.

Chapter Thirty

I'ma Survivor

Roxanne pulled in alongside the red Chevy Nova, glad to know Malik hadn't left yet. She wanted to see his face when she told him he'd get an extra thousand dollars off each kilo. The house smelled of cookies. She could hear his voice. He was in the kitchen, telling someone he'd bake cookies for them. Promising to bring with him the cookies he was baking now.

"Hey," said Roxanne, low, with a wave of a jeweled hand. She stopped at the door of the kitchen. Malik smiled, glad to see her. Her smile said she was glad to see him too.

"See you in a few, Miss Universe," he said into the phone, smiling.

Roxanne saw a new man. "You gotta little playboy in you, huh," she said.

"Naw. I ain't no playboy," replied Malik. "Made some cookies while I waited. Want some chocolate chip?"

Roxanne nodded, sitting at the dining room table. "You ain't gonna guess who I saw at Michael's funeral," she said as Malik placed a glass of milk before her.

"Who's that?"

"Freeway Rick," she replied. "He's shady," she added.

Malik felt as if he was in a different orbit than Freeway Rick. A safer orbit with his own new friends and situations that he couldn't have imagined existed. Selling dope was more than opening a crack house and taking risks with every daily sale.

"Was Michael cool with Freeway?" asked Malik, bringing back a plate of soft, warm chocolate chip cookies.

"Apparently not, but I thought they were cool," replied Roxanne, taking a bite of the cookie.

"I'd keep my eyes on Hill," said Malik. "He might be plotting on you."

"Don't Shoota know Hill?" she asked.

Malik's eyes flashed with the memory of Shoota telling him that Hill wanted to rob Roxanne. "Yeh, he be connecting with them more lately," he said, not wanting to share Shoota's support of the plot with her.

"I think they tryna set him up. They bought a lot of dope from him or you?" she asked, just now considering that they could very well be trying to set Shoota up. Rob and kill him, then collect their fee. Roxanne gasped with this thought.

"Yeh. They asked him for a couple kilos for ten each, but I ain't really feeling them cats."

Roxanne nodded. She could see that they'd already

gotten close to Shoota.

"So, word is that Hill plotting on you," said Malik. "And you say they plotting on Shoota."

Roxanne nodded.

"Look like we need to watch out for Hill and his brother," said Malik.

"How would you feel if Shoota could do his thang in L.A.," she began. "Give him a good price. Let him be a big man on campus."

Malik could see it. Shoota would be occupied and have enough money to cool his envy.

"Let's settle on from now on," began Roxanne, touching Malik on the hand across the table, "you get everything over seven." She smiled.

Malik nodded. "That'll work," he said, doing the quick math. It was all too much money. The comfort lay in the fact that he could do what he wished and pay for what he wanted.

This also solved the Shoota problem. "I'ma let Shoota know to watch Hill, tho," he said.

"You do that. I really want him to be cool with me," she said. "I don't know why he hates me."

"How you know that? He don't even know you."

"I just always got a weird vibe from him. But maybe you're right. We should all three do something together."

This sounded good, but Malik didn't trust it would ever happen. Something had to be done about Hill, he thought to himself. Shoota was the best person to make that happen.

"So, I think maybe you'll need extra work," said Roxanne. "Take my work with you. If you need more for my local people just get more. They'll wait the extra day."

Malik suspected that Roxanne was shook up in a way. He wondered if what was at play were the wheels turning for what Joseph referred to as her being out the way. Malik negotiated in his mind how he can best share this obscure threat with her, but found that he'd rather not gossip, making it his business.

"I'll take what I can get off for sure. That still leaves twenty for Cookie that I can keep here," he agreed, partly as the favor she needed. The other part was obviously having access to more cocaine at a better price. "And still give me a few days to get back," he added.

She agreed, reluctantly having to keep dope in the house. She hadn't foreseen the possibility of this inconvenience. Malik shared with her his plans to start basketball camp. He didn't share his living situation, leaving her to assume he'd be around mostly. He didn't share that he'd bought a low-rider either. Malik was content to share this only with Elisa.

"You're so thoughtful... cookies and milk," Roxanne said from the back porch as Malik got in his car to leave after reloading Roxanne's cocaine.

"See you in a couple days," he said, backing from her in the dirt driveway.

Roxanne felt lucky. Malik was proving to be a real asset. She loved that he actually felt like her ideas were well thought through. She admired his intelligence. Long after Malik left the house, she sensed a presence.

Roxanne slipped into the bedroom and grabbed up her personal bag of cocaine. She celebrated her survival of an assassination attempt and bringing enemies closer with a few lines of cocaine.

The first line shocked her, scrambling her sinuses. The second line rang a bell in her head. The third line made her skin pulse and the light around her brighter.

Chapter Thirty-One

What's Done In The Dark

Malik felt like a man returning to his secret place to indulge in a secret life. With secret money and a secret woman with secret knowledge about secret places and secret things. He pulled into the apartment parking spot, right before the front door, and killed the engine on a secret car with secret deposits of cocaine in the secret trunk. The only question was, like his grandfather always said, *How long before what's done in the dark come into the light.*

Elisa had the door open for him as he entered with a single leather satchel of bound stacks of money. Leftovers from loose sales of cocaine through the city, Dutch, being the main person.

"I love when you come home," said Elisa, her shiny onyx-hued body pressing against a purple silk nightgown. Her tight breasts bubbled to a defined collar bone and dipped and curved to a soft sensual neck.

"I like your hair," he said, leaning to her exposed neck and kissing the scented skin.

"Well, I needed it out the way because I was cooking."

Malik scanned the room quickly. After nearly a month, the apartment had taken on their character. It was appointed with African art, fine linens, and plenty of good food.

"What you cook?" he asked, the familiar smell of vegetarian cabbage in the air.

"Your favorite," she replied. "Remember when you thought I ate this way because you thought I was poor?" She laughed out.

"That wasn't me," he said jokingly, grabbing her in his embrace. "You would assume such a thing?"

"Yeh, right." She laughed under his assault of kisses along her warming neck.

"I was wrong about everything," he whispered. "But right about you," he added.

"I added cashews to the cabbage. And more bean meat."

Malik had distrusted the bean meat. He thought there could be no substitute for righteous meatball. But then he ate her vegetarian cabbage.

"That's exactly what I hoped it was," he said, kissing her on the lips.

"You want to make love now or would you rather eat first?" asked Elisa, her eyes smoky.

Malik kissed her again, slowly, his hands caressing her tight ass beneath the silk. She was firm to the touch, along her hips and thighs.

"Eat. Let me bathe you," she whispered. "Let's sit. Tell me about your day."

Malik followed the languid motion of her smooth dark arm. On the table was a fresh, steaming plate of vegetarian cabbage with huge hunks of bean meat throughout.

"And I love you long time," she sung like a Korean massage parlor worker.

With Elisa, Malik shared his relationship with Shoota and his mistrust of him. He shared his conversations with Roxanne and the things he left out about Shoota agreeing to rob her.

Elisa listened with fine attention, as if learning the characters of a fantastic play. A play that was led by the man she loved. The most fantastic character of them all.

"My low-rider coming in the morning," said Malik, watching her from the bed, hours after dinner and a story about Dutch, the tailored man from across the street.

"I like Dutch," said Elisa, climbing into bed with Malik.

"Yeh, he's cool," agreed Malik, remembering only months ago that he was impressed by Dutch. Still was, but not for the same reasons.

"Would Dutch be someone you'd bring out here?" asked Elisa.

Malik had never considered this, but thinking on it he realized he might be the one person he could share this secret life with. "Yeh," he said. "We invite him to the next party Joseph throw."

"Oh, the way you describe him that crowd will want to suck him dry."

Malik chuckled.

"Serious. White people love their rare birds. They like their colors. And you never know what they might say," she added.

"Most people just say we monkeys," said Malik, rubbing along her hip.

Elisa snuggled against him. "I know," she said low. "My mother is Hawaiian. I like flowers and birds."

Malik enjoyed the feel, scent, and move of her soft, firm body as she fit against him. He closed his eyes, the soft jazz playing from the living room soothing his senses. He felt her mouth on him, kissing his chest, then moving down.

She sucked him into her mouth, growing him stiff on her tongue before sliding up and putting him inside her. She fit snug over him, opening with each slow grind.

Malik's entire body felt her touch. He gripped her thighs as she rode him, his eyes closed, feeling the completeness of her full pussy. Exploding inside her was an ongoing sensation as she milked, grinded, and brought him back to stiffness for more slow grinding.

Chapter Thirty-Two

Drug Induced Haze

It's all gonna work out, whispered Roxanne into the mound of powder cocaine before her. Stripped of all her jewelry it lay strewn on the table, gleaming and sparkling gold and diamonds, a frame to the cocaine monument. It was too heavy, she'd felt. The jingling and jangling of her Turkish ropes sounded like wind chimes. They kept dipping onto the cocaine when she'd dipped her nose to the mound.

Roxanne whispered affirmations to herself despite feeling as lonely as a frog on a lily pad. She'd wanted Malik to stay. She thought of calling him. *I'm high*, she murmured, then laughed out loud.

Just as her laughing subsided she heard the familiar creaking of the floor just inside the back door.

"Malik," she called out, struggling to stand from her chair. There was no answer. The creaking sound was slow. She slowly grabbed the .380 which lay on the table beside her many diamond tennis bracelets and gold bangles.

Roxanne remained still, listening, wondering if she was being paranoid. Then there was the familiar creak again. She swore she heard breathing, but doubted the cocaine had increased her hearing to superhero status. She laughed at this thought, loosely gripping the pistol.

Then she saw the shadow cross to the side of her, sprinting across the hallway entrance. She watched the brightly lit hallway for another figure, thinking she might've been tripping.

"Malik," she said, her heart beating hard. She worked to control her breathing. Then there was the gleam of a pistol. Roxanne pointed her gun towards the barrel, waiting for the body, hoping it was a hallucination. The barrel of the black gun swung in slow motion from the hallway. Then there was another from the other side. Roxanne swung her gun wildly, pulling the trigger at the cocaine ghosts. Her body jerked, hot fire piercing her shoulder.

Bow legs, her thoughts sang as she fell back into the table, those legs marching towards her, the spark of the pistol shutting her eyes. Roxanne squeezed again and again, sometimes hearing the grunt of the bullet tearing through flesh. She felt a sharp breath shoot to her with the final squeeze of a trigger.

Roxanne felt several pockets of hot fire coursing through her body, spilling to the hardwood floor before her. The sound of the squeezing echoes over the last sounds of scrambling feet and whispers.

My nigga... Bitch got me...You hit? Bitch got me...
Where the shit at? Bitch got me... Bitch... Got it ...

Roxanne could barely hear her own breathing. She concentrated on her shallow wheeze. The voices had departed. It was silent. Except for the fading wheeze and hot blood spilling from her body. She could only see the dark. And feel the light.

Chapter Thirty-Three

Grindin' To The Top

Malik was up like a soldier in the armed forces. Pearl was his first stop before eight in the morning. The projects were sleepy, hardly any movement. Through the winding streets, Malik remembered landmarks to distinguish one indistinct twenty unit apartment complex from the other; at this corner there was a rusted Oldsmobile with a cracked front windshield. On the next corner was a bright blue mailbox scrawled with graffiti detailing this project's gang loyalty: Bloods.

　　Malik knew he was getting closer to Pearl's complex by the look of the cars lining the sidewalk. They were getting shinier. And there was more movement. Mothers were up warming their cars for the drive to work or to school to drop their children off for a day of learning and mischief. Malik recognized the line of undented, shiny cars lining the curb when he made a turn onto a trash-free street. Security seemed to be tighter here. At the corner complex a group of aware young men inspected Malik as he passed by.

Malik was impressed by Pearl from their last meeting. He'd at first doubted her and then misjudged her for her apparent preference for the affection of women over men. He'd remained conservative at their earlier meeting, having never met anyone like her. The male garments at first fooled him, but her mannerisms alerted him to something he'd never witnessed before. But then there were the subtle signals that she was open to a man's touch.

Even now, Malik looked forward to seeing her. She was a mystery. An enigma. Someone courageous and obviously in possession of what most referred to as the quality which propelled folks to leadership. Malik was intrigued by her and privately wondered how she and Roxanne had become acquainted.

Malik tried to imagine how much territory Pearl actually controlled and influenced. He compared her to Roxanne as being a female dope dealer, but there was more to Pearl, he realized, feeling motivated to get to know her better. Her demeanor and outward flamboyance and aggressiveness he sensed, covered room for a real one to occupy in a real way.

Outside Pearl's unit were two grimy teenagers, huddled in red parkas, their hooded eyes watching Malik with a mix of familiarity and caution. He pulled to the curb under their watchful eyes. He took his time as if he belonged, waiting out their patience for him to emerge from the stock, clean Chevy Nova.

With the boldness of an emerging boss, privately willing the two young thugs, undoubtedly near the same age as him, to respect his deliberate movements without question, Malik slowly emerged from the car. He nodded to the alert guards with respect, dissolving any suspicions they might have and gaining any good will they were capable of providing.

With the knowledge that a just awakened Pearl awaited him and the fact that he was in protected territory, he grabbed the duffel bag of cocaine and money counter from the trunk. Once the money was right it was nothing to grab the dope. Malik stepped with confidence through the grill security gate, giving a solid nod of acknowledgment to the young guards, and to Pearl's second floor door.

Malik awaited the greeting after knocking the appropriate warning of his presence. He looked to the courtyard. The place where a swimming pool was meant to be was nothing more than an empty basin littered with bicycle parts, children's toys, and environmental debris.

The door opened suddenly. He was surprised. He'd expected to hear someone ask who it was or something close, but instead he was met by a shapely young woman in nothing more than a t-shirt. Malik doubted she had on any panties.

"Hi," the teenaged, light-skinned girl said, her breasts pressing hard against her fresh wife-beater. "Malik?"

The sound of his name in the mouth of this beautiful, minutes from sleep, pouty-mouthed girl, was a welcomed invitation as she stepped aside to receive him. She smiled both invitingly and with fatigue and interest as he entered. The front room was decorated with fat leather couches, a salt-water fish tank and semi-nude women laying next to, across, and atop each other.

"We be doin' us," the tender, young, beautiful girl said, gesturing towards the hallway, expecting Malik.

"Right on," said Malik, controlling his youthful desire for her deliciousness as he passed to the hallway.

Not to his surprise Pearl was lifting herself from two naked women, their ample asses poking and raising with seductive invitation from the mattress.

"Hey, mister man," Pearl said, squinting her eyes as if in apology for her late rising.

"Wassup," replied Malik, not sure how masculine to be given her gangsta. "Am I too early," he added, reminding himself that she'd agreed to the early morning.

"Aw naw," she began, "it's cool."

Malik watched as her ample cinnamon breasts spilled at the edges of a sheer wife-beater. "Wanna jump in," she said, smiling, joking, as she passed, looking to the sleeping women behind her on the bed.

Malik inhaled her sex scent, his eyes tearing themselves from the beautiful shapes on the bed. They moved sexually, sensing new eyes on them. He marveled at the casualness of the arrangement.

Malik was in the living room, witnessing the awakening of Pearl's most intimate domain. The women, strewn amongst the fat leather sofas and lounge chairs, untangled, yawned, and opened their eyes to a new, sometimes familiar face, some placing where they'd seen Malik before.

Pearl emerged from the hallway as if a brand new woman, smiling and calculating as the apartment came to life.

"It was a long night," said Pearl, her plain white t-shirt doing nothing to hide the full plumpness of her breasts. She stood in front of him in the living room.

"I feel you," said Malik, hating that he'd seen her so early, waking from sleep and in the company of two women.

"Come," she said, motioning him to follow her. "We can handle our business in here."

Malik followed her through the hallway and to a closed door. She opened it, saying, "They be gettin' up when they feel like it."

On the low bed, in the middle of the room, two women were fucking doggy style, the big booty white girl taking it from a big booty black girl from the back. They were caught up in their own world, having not heard or cared for the opening of the bedroom door.

"Hold up," said Pearl, walking towards the closet, skirting the squeaking bed.

Malik tried to ignore the lesbian sex happening on the bed. The white girl, with a nice ass, was throwing her booty back as if on a real dick. She was whimpering and moaning as her fucker slammed the strapped dildo inside of her.

"Got it," said Pearl, holding up a heavy-duty trash bag as she approached him, seemingly ignoring the sexual action on the bed.

Malik fed the money through the money counter as Pearl directed a curvaceous dark-skinned woman to make breakfast for the house before she disappeared to take a shower.

The cocaine Pearl had paid for was sitting near the glass coffee table when she finally joined him wearing a fresh pair of jeans and a Kings hockey jersey.

"I like you," said Pearl, sitting next to him on the emptied couch, breaking into a brick of cocaine.

Pearl chipped off a bit of powder and put it to her nose. "Perfect after a night of drinking," she said, rubbing the cocaine across her gums and sucking the rest off of her finger.

Malik couldn't help but to agree, silently watching as she absorbed the effect of the cocaine. She snorted and tossed her head back. When she finally recovered, looking to Malik, she grinned.

"Straight?" asked Malik.

Pearl nodded, grinning her satisfaction. "Can I ask you a question," she asked, her eyes low and seductive.

Malik nodded, taking her cue to relax, leaning back on the couch as near naked women appeared and disappeared around the edges of the room.

"You in it for real with Roxy?" asked Pearl.

Malik wasn't sure what she meant. Pearl's dark eyes gave nothing away as she studied him casually.

Pearl smiled. "I'm just being nosey," she said. "I'm nasty, that's all."

Malik understood now. "Naw, I got a girl," he said, thinking of Trinity and the look on her face when she had said she was pregnant.

Pearl grinned. "I can tell just by looking at you that she fly," she said.

"She cool."

"I bet you got a few girls, huh?"

Malik didn't want to admit the truth of this. "I try to keep it simple," he replied, leaning to refill the money counter.

"So, you ain't never had a threesome?" she asked, looking at him seductively.

Malik saw Pearl regularly sleeping with multiple women. "Nope," he admitted.

She smiled. "Well, we gonna have to do something about that," she said. "You down?"

Malik knew he shouldn't be down, but he wanted to be down. "Maybe," he said, refilling the money counter. He liked her smile. He liked the softness under her masculine demeanor.

"You can pick any girl here as long as I'm included," she said. "And don't think I'm some kind of hoe or nothing, but I just want to see what it do with you."

Malik found himself drawn to Pearl. She was a sweet mixture of feminine gestures and boyish aggression. She knew what she wanted and went after it. There was no mistaking her beauty.

The money counter finished shuffling. Malik was partly glad because though he was enjoying her company, he had one more stop to make.

"We might be able to complete my fantasy," he said, gathering up the money.

"That's it right there." She smiled out. "Roxanne told me to leave you be," she added. "So, what we do beyond our business is between me and you, okay?"

"Of course," assured Malik, rising to leave.

"I wish you could chill right now," said Pearl, following him to the door. "Give Roxy a hug for me when you see her."

Malik assured Pearl that he would as he stepped from her door carrying a duffel bag full of money.

Chapter Thirty-Four

Getting Closer To The Truth

Malik arrived at the door of Jamaica Rob's after a quick trip to Victor, giving him five kilos, much less than what Jamaica had ordered. Malik doubted that Victor had the out of town connections that Jamaica spoke of having. When the front door of the small apartment opened Malik was met by the smiling face of Rob's little sister and the smell of bacon.

"Who at my door, Serena?" asked Rob's mother, appearing behind the girl, walking from the kitchen into the living room. She smiled when she saw Malik and the duffel bag of dope and money counter slung over his shoulder.

"Hi, Serena," said Malik to the bright-eyed chocolate girl, her hair hanging in long, rust-colored dreadlocks.

"You my brother's friend?" asked Serena, giving a lot of weight to the word, *friend.*

"Yes, I am," replied Malik. Serena smiled.

"Let him in and close the door, Serena," said Rob's mother, waving to Malik as he stepped inside. "Good morning, baby," she added to Malik.

"Good morning, Miss Rob."

She smiled. "Call me Sharon, baby," she said. "He in the room probably still asleep. Go wake him up and I'll bring y'all breakfast. You hungry?"

Malik was thirsty for some reason. The bacon smelled good. Elisa had gotten up with him, prepared to make him breakfast. He'd promised to be back soon and eat then.

"Okay," he said, feeling like an intruder for the way Rob's mother was dressed in a sheer t-shirt that stopped at her pretty thighs, doing a minimal job to hide her shapely figure and fat nipple breasts.

"Want milk or orange juice?" asked Serena, looking up to Malik with a happy face, poised to spring into action.

"Orange juice will be cool," he said, watching her scramble off.

"Girl, you better slow down," said her mother as Serena slowed to a walk nearing the kitchen.

Malik tapped on Rob's door. It crept open with the pressure of his knocking. Beside Rob, who was looking up at him, grinning, from a low bed, was a shapely woman.

"Come on in," said Rob, tapping the bare ass of the woman next to him. "We got bidness. Go out," he said to his little sister.

The woman moved sensuously next to him, reaching beneath the cover to massage his rippled stomach.

"Robert," called his little sister from the opened door,

peering around Malik. "Ma said to get ready for breakfast." She handed Malik the glass of orange juice she was holding.

The woman next to Rob stirred further, reaching to his dick beneath the covers. "Okay, close the door," he responded to his sister.

The woman disappeared under the covers when the door closed. She found his dick and began sucking.

Rob grinned, shrugging. "Grab duh money from da closet mahn," said Rob, pointing to a closed door along the wall.

There were several trash bags stuffed inside the closet amidst boxes of shoes and hanging clothes. The small space was cramped. "Which one?" asked Malik, looking to Rob. The woman had increased her head bobbing under the cover.

"Any one, bruh," he replied. "We count it all up."

Malik grabbed a trash bag filled with rubber-banded stacks of money. He sat at a small desk in the corner of the room, ignoring the woman who'd moved the cover back, exposing her morning head game.

"Yo, bruh," said Rob, behind Malik as he loaded the money counter. "Each one a grand. Trust me, rude mahn."

Malik does trust him. He'd resolved to count stacks at random. The sound of the clicking and whirring competes with the sucking sounds the woman makes on Rob's dick. She slowed to massage the head as he released inside her mouth.

"Oh, shit," Rob groaned when she popped off his dick.

Malik stared at the shuffling money in the counter as the woman hopped energetically from the bed. She pulled on a pair of tight jeans and a basketball jersey that was too big.

"Hi," she said to Malik as if he'd not just witnessed her sucking dick and seen her naked. "You want breakfast too, right?" she asked.

Malik struggled to answer, shook by her plain beauty and boldness. "Yeh. Thanks," he managed.

"Coming right up." She spun on her heels and walked out the room.

"She's good, mahn," said Rob, smiling mischievously.

"I believe you," said Malik as Rob swung his legs to the floor and stood naked.

"Brand new day, rude mahn," said Rob, slipping on a pair of boxers and baggy jeans. "You still got some of dem trees?" he asked.

Malik said, "Yeh," before sharing with him how Elisa had refused to smoke more after she nearly coughed up her lungs.

Rob enjoyed hearing this news, laughing as he pulled a shoebox from under his bed. Inside were tightly compacted small Christmas trees of silver haired marijuana.

"She not gonna like this," he said, handing Malik a fistful of the buds.

The aroma of the buds invaded Malik's nostrils. "I told her to take smaller puffs," said Malik.

"Even smaller with dem, bruh," Rob said this seriously, breaking apart a bud and dropping its small knots of weed along a fat zig-zag. "We going to Spokane, bruh. Them thangs go for damn near twenty up there," he said, kicking the duffel bag of dope at his feet.

Rob's sister opened the door, her eyes scanning the room quickly, stopping briefly on Malik and the silent money machine. "Cumberland at the door," she said to Rob. "He say come out."

"What he want nosey 'cuz you know," he said to her.

She made a motion to deny that she knew anything before wilting under his sure gaze upon her. "Reese out there," she said this low, transferring the urgency of Cumberland's visit.

Rob slammed a fist into his open palm. "Come on, bruh," he said to Malik. "We settle in a few minutes."

Malik looked around the room, unsure of leaving the money and dope in plain sight. "What's going on?" he wanted to know.

"This be short," assured Rob, already heading out the door.

"Robert!" called his mother as Malik followed him through the living room towards the front door. "Breakfast first, boy."

"One minute, Ma," he replied, holding up a finger as he stepped through the door.

Outside, a small crowd of men had formed. Malik recognized them as the core of Rob's closest friends. In the middle of them was a tall man with short dreadlocks. He looked to Rob.

"Reese, boy," said Rob, striding up casually as the circle opened for him, the fat joint dangling from his lips.

"It wasn't my fault," began the frightened man. "Dem fags snuck me. Wasn't nothing I could do."

"I say mahn not to go over there," said Rob. "That's your fault, mahn." With this said he nodded to the muscular man beside him.

Before Reese could protest the muscular man smashed his fists into his face, forcing spouts of blood from fresh cuts. His nose flowed a river of blood. The smacking sounds of fists meeting flesh echoed in the morning air.

When Reese fell to the ground he was stomped on until he was nearly motionless. Rob broke it up before the man was sure to fall unconscious. He lifted the dizzy man off the ground, brushing off dirt and grass from his disheveled clothes.

"Listen next time, bruddah," said Rob, placing his palm on the back of the man's neck, holding him in place. "Listen," he repeated.

The man nodded, obviously thankful for Rob's forgiveness. The crowd then accepted the man into the fold. Rob handed Reese the fat joint hanging from his lips.

Malik didn't ask what the beat down was about. Breakfast was waiting for them when they went back inside Rob's house. He couldn't believe how hungry he was, reasoning he'd have to eat again when he got back to Elisa. She was surely waiting to eat until he arrived.

Malik's meeting with Jamaica Rob only confirmed their initial bond. When Malik suggested that Rob return to the USC sponsored basketball camp as his playing partner, both looked forward to it. Shoota's name wasn't mentioned once. Malik wondered how close they were in the first place.

Malik privately wondered what effect Rob would have at one of Joseph's parties. Another rare and colorful bird indeed.

Chapter Thirty-Five

My Two Lives

Elisa had a breakfast of chicken omelets and hash browns waiting for Malik when he walked through the front door. She was beaming with some private knowledge that he waited patiently for her to reveal.

"So, tell me how you got blood on your shirt?" she asked, watching him from the edge of the kitchen as she brought him more cranberry juice.

Malik couldn't imagine how he was close enough to Reese's beat down to get blood on him. He explained to her what happened at Jamaica Rob's house, leaving out the part about seeing his woman give him head and walk around naked, though she'd probably think nothing of it.

"That's crazy," said Elisa. "Rob sounds like he runs a tight ship."

"Yeh. He play ball, too. He gonna come to camp with me," said Malik.

Elisa studied Malik, her chin in the palm of her hand. "You two sound close," she said, but to Malik it felt like she wanted to say something else. "Will I ever meet him?"

Malik considered this. He'd thought about inviting Rob to one of Joseph's parties. "You think he would like Joseph and his friends? "

"Does he need a translator?" she asked, smiling.

Malik grinned. "Probably... Naw. He'll be cool though. He like those colorful birds you talk about white people liking to have around."

"Sounds like my kinda guy."

Malik looked to her amused expression. "You tryna make me jealous?"

She smiled with mischief. "Never, baby." She rose and made room for herself on his thigh at the table. She enjoyed the feel of his palm on her ass.

Malik was sure she was about to say something she'd been holding back all morning when someone knocked at the front door.

"That's probably my car," he said.

"Car?" asked Elisa, moving from his lap.

"You'll see. Come on."

Elisa followed him to the front door where a muscular, tattooed, white man was standing with a clipboard in his hand. He was wearing blue khaki overalls. Behind him, sitting idle in the small parking lot was a flatbed truck. Sitting like a prized jewel in the air was a gleaming, black on black, convertible 1965 Chevy Impala SS, its shiny tires nimble, standing like ballerina slippers around chrome spoke rims.

"Ohh my," gasped Elisa beside Malik.

"What I tell you," whispered Malik, accepting the clipboard from the bearded white man.

"It's beautiful," replied Elisa, stepping outside for a closer look.

All the white neighbors immediately fell in love with Malik's special toy. They'd assembled to watch the unloading of the shiny car from the flatbed truck.

Malik felt Elisa's touch on his shoulder as he thanked another white person's compliment about the car.

"I always thought dudes like Dutch were rich," Malik said. "But now I realize even he's poor."

"It's just an illusion."

"True. He live good. But not good like Joseph," said Malik.

"The only good that matter is our good. And our good ain't bad," Elisa whispered softly.

Malik agreed, leaning to kiss her on the forehead.

"Malik," began Elisa, looking into his eyes. "I love you."

"I love you, too," he responded, realizing how very much possible it was to love two women at the same time.

She smiled. "What time does Joseph want you there?"

"It's a night pool party, he say. You rolling, right?" said Malik.

"Is that an invitation?" she said, her black eyes sparkling.

"Of course. You and them the same type people. I need you to translate," he replied, smiling with her gentle nudge.

"Well, I need to share something with you before we go," she said a bit more seriously.

Malik had never seen this smoky shade of black in her eyes before.

"I'm pregnant," she said simply, watching for his reaction.

A slow smile spread across his lips. *This boy will have my name, Malik,* he thought to himself. "Perfect," he said to Elisa.

She smiled, grateful for his joy. "Is this something that you want?"

"More than life itself," he said. "Like you said, 'We doin' it one hundred percent', right?"

"One hundred percent," she agreed.

"Wanna go for a ride?"

Elisa smiled wide. She'd never been in a low-rider.

Chapter Thirty-Six

More Traces Of Death

The first call came from Trinity. Malik was in the low-rider, waiting for Elisa and the short drive up the graveled drive to Joseph's girlfriend's house. He couldn't wait to see the look on Joseph's face when he saw it.

Trinity called to share the news that Shoota was found dead behind the Ralph's market on Vernon and Figueroa. He'd been shot several times. Apparently word was that he'd been dropped off there. By who, no one knew.

Malik was not surprised by Shoota's death. He couldn't imagine how he would end up dead in the back of a grocery store. He didn't share this with Elisa on the way into the woods of Lytle Creek.

"Is everything okay?" asked Elisa when Malik ended the bad news call. Malik was a mix of emotions, trying to quell the tears of loss. He wondered if it was his fault. He'd left him in L.A. to let the streets deal with his thirst and envy.

"We should go back, baby," suggested Elisa, noticing the grief overtaking him. Malik pulled to the small rest stop off the shoulder of the narrow graveled road. He exhaled powerfully, wiping at his eyes to prevent the tears.

"My best friend was killed," he said after taking a deep breath and looking out to the woods beyond, cabins hidden high amongst the foliage.

"Shoota?" she asked, touching him lightly on the shoulder.

Malik nodded, remembering that Roxanne spoke of birth replacing death when he'd told her that Trinity was pregnant not long after the death of his grandfather. Now Elisa was pregnant and Shoota was dead.

"Yeh," he breathed out slowly, wiping at his eyes.

"Should you go to L.A.?" asked Elisa.

Malik considered this, but decided there was nothing for him to do. He was caught with a fear that he may have been involved with Hill, doing something he didn't have to do.

"Naw, we good," he said, touching her stomach lightly.

"Whatever you need from me I'm here for you," she assured Malik before leaning over to share a tight hug and kiss.

Malik attempted a brave smile. "Thanks," he responded, reluctant to leave her after learning that she was pregnant. "You ready for the pool party?"

Elisa shared his resolve. "If you are," she said.

Malik took another deep breath. "We good," he assured

her, pulling back onto the road for the short drive to Joseph's gathering.

The second call came while Malik was sitting with Joseph at the far corner of the shimmering swimming pool. Before them were lean men and women playing water volleyball.

Elisa was near the bar, across the swimming pool, with Joseph's girlfriend and two more slender white women. Elisa looked over from time to time, between polite conversation and gentle laughter, making eye contact with Malik.

"She's out the way," said Joseph, leaning forward across the table. His portable phone was held away from his ear, still smoking with the news.

"Huh?" asked Malik, his attention caught by Elisa, seeing her anew, as the mother of his child. The players in the pool cheered and splashed between them.

"That was Saul," began Joseph, his face looking serious. "Roxy's been shot up." He stared at Malik for a reaction.

Roxy. It sounded funny coming from Joseph, Malik thought to himself. He was not surprised to hear this. "Where is she?" he wanted to know, praying Joseph didn't say she was dead.

"In Mercy General. They put her in a coma. Intensive Care," Joseph said this quickly as Malik stood from his seat. "She can't have visitors," said Joseph, motioning Malik back to his seat.

"We'll all go in the morning," added Joseph. "Saul has called her mother. Tons of family will be there."

I'm family, he thought to himself. *She ain't never in the way.* Elisa looked to him, catching his eyes. She waved for him to come to her.

"Saul will be there in the morning," Joseph was saying. "Looks like you'll be running it."

Malik heard him, watching Elisa excuse herself. He

turned to Joseph. "I gotta roll," he said.

Joseph waved him off. "Sure. Of course. Go."

Malik met Elisa near the pool. He knew nothing would ever be the same for them.

Chapter Thirty-Seven

Family Ties

Malik's mind was swimming with wild thoughts. It couldn't be a coincidence that Shoota was dead and Roxanne was in the hospital. But how Shoota ended up behind a supermarket eluded him. The strong dank smoke of the herbs that Jamaica gave him soothed his angst and worry. The powerful engine of the Chevy Nova pushed hard as the tires chewed up the highway in the fast lane, the night masking his watery eyes and marijuana smoke.

Please don't let her die, Malik prayed, feeling for the first time her generosity and goodness. *She doesn't deserve this,* he whispered around the dank smoke, the skyline of Mercy General Hospital visible from the freeway.

Malik was silently glad that Elisa didn't insist on coming with him. She understood perfectly that affairs beyond explanation had to be tended to. Malik could still see the concern and worry in her eyes as she stood in the open door after kissing him tenderly.

"Come back to me," she'd said.

"I will," Malik promised, putting his palm to her stomach and their unborn child.

The parking lot of the hospital showed a mix of cars belonging to regular working folks; and shiny cars with designer paint, rims, and tires that signified its owners as good hustlers or drug dealers.

Malik found a parking spot near the rear of the crowded parking lot. He waited a few minutes before getting out the car, taking time to collect himself in preparation for what he might see. He didn't know what to expect.

Malik called Trinity, responding to her page. He'd said he would call her when he got to the city. He'd forgotten, his mind on everything else but her.

"Hey you," said Trinity, concern etched in her voice.

"Hi. I just got to the hospital," he said, looking out to the parking lot of stationary cars, sitting like caskets for the walking dead.

Trinity was silent for a few beats before she said, "I hope she's okay."

"Yeh, me too." And he really did. He couldn't imagine things staying the same without her.

"Do you know if she's awake or..."

"Joseph said she in a coma or something. But Saul is supposed to be there so I'ma see what's up," he said. "Mom good?" he asked, wanting to switch subjects.

"Yeh," assured Trinity. "Now she won't let me go home.

I damn near got all my clothes here," she said this lightly.

Malik felt something else in her tone. He felt that maybe she suspected there was a woman in San Bernardino. Maybe she wanted to ask why was it that he spent so many nights away.

"Crazy 'cuz at first she was on some 'when she going home' hype," he said lightly, grinning with the memory and feeling good talking to Trinity, reminded of their love and devotion.

"She ain't on that no more," said Trinity. "She all about how is the baby now." She chuckled. "I try to remind her it's just two months. Everything is fine."

"She need somebody to look after," said Malik, thinking of how she used to fuss over his grandfather, making sure he ate right and took his heart pills.

"For real." Laughed Trinity. "She stay on me about making sure I eat for the baby." Malik smiled with this, envisioning his mother peeking into his room and questioning Trinity, waking her from sleep to do so.

"Let me get in here," he said after a moment of thoughtful silence. "I'm on my way home after I see what's what with Roxy."

The night air was crisp and quiet. He imagined that the hospital was a somber place. He hoped the lobby wasn't filled with gang members and raucous relatives. His pace was slow as he smoked on the last of the strong herbs.

He saw himself from above, dressed in crisp Dockers and Sperry Top-Sider boat shoes. His collared Polo button-up shirt completed the square college look. No doubt Trinity would again be suspicious as to who might be influencing his dress code.

"Waddup, G," a man's voice said from the darkness before stepping from a long, brightly painted Cadillac Brougham.

Malik recognized him, but dared not let on that he knew the drug dealer. He was not surprised to find Freeway Rick there at the hospital.

"Wassup, folks," replied Malik, slowing his steps, blowing out a slim stream of marijuana smoke.

"Got some more of that?" asked Rick, his Turkish ropes and diamond encrusted Cadillac medallion gleaming in the night.

"This it right here," replied Malik, handing the last of the fat joint to his outstretched fingers.

"I seen you around, ain't I?" he asked, taking a soft pull of the short joint. "This some good shit right here."

Malik remained silent, taking a step away towards the hospital entrance.

"You Roxy folks, right?" asked Rick, staying in place.

Malik stopped. "Yeh," he said. "She's a friend of mine."

Freeway Rick nodded knowingly, taking another hit of the joint. "This shit real good," he said. "You got more of this?"

"Naw," he replied. "Somebody gave that to me."

Freeway nodded. "Awright, youngsta," he said. "Roxanne might not make it."

Malik felt a hollowness swim through him. He wanted to tell this man to shut up, instead he nodded quietly and resumed his steps towards the hospital.

"I'm Freeway Rick, youngsta. If you need anything just holla when you see me."

"My name is Malik. Right on, bro."

"I already know," said Rick. "Give my best to Roxy."

Malik didn't respond. He tried to remember if Roxanne had ever mentioned Freeway Rick. Having spoken with him Malik now realized he'd given the man too much consideration.

The lobby of the hospital was occupied by exactly

what the cars in the lot promised. Along a back wall sat what looked to be the family and relatives of someone who was important. They were dressed fashionably. They all looked like they were waiting with anxiety for any news of a loved one.

On the opposite end of the room was a large family of white people, the oldest of them, a gray-haired man, walked back and forth before the assembled group, looking anxiously towards a set of plain white double doors at the front of the room.

"Malik," said a familiar voice, stepping up beside him, her eyes were red from fresh tears.

"Hey, Nisha," replied Malik, regretting that he'd never said more than hello the many times he'd walked into the salon. "How's Roxanne?"

"She just got out of surgery," said Nisha, holding back tears. "They say she might not..." she stopped, her eyes brimming with fresh tears.

The family against the far wall looked on with interest while Nisha attempted to control her anguish.

"Who would do this to her?" she asked, the tears flowing over and wetting her face.

Malik could only guess, but he had a good idea.

"She never hurt anybody," she cried, fresh tears coming from her eyes.

Malik took her in his arms, her body shuddering against him as she cried. No one paid attention to them standing in the middle of the room. He doubted anyone could see Roxanne now. He suspected that the fine-looking family along the back wall belonged to Roxanne. He recognized the young boy on the lap of an older woman. He couldn't remember his name. He was Roxanne's son. Seeing him angered Malik, knowing that his mother would perhaps not live through the night.

Chapter Thirty-Eight

The Smell Of Blood

Malik's dislike for hospitals had grown. Leaving the doors, the night air filling his lungs, he took a big gulp. His steps were unsure, the grief of imagining how Roxanne must've looked and felt overtaking him. Malik steadied himself in the cool night air, resolved to make it to his car. *There's got to be a connection,* he thought to himself. *Shoota dead and Roxanne in the hospital.*

He took on long, deliberate strides through the parking lot, thankful that Freeway Rick was no longer parked on the way to his car. He sat behind the wheel, his mind turning at the coincidence of it all. He slammed his fists against the steering wheel, frustrated with himself for not taking Shoota with him.

Roxanne might still be... He abandoned this thought, disappointed at what he was about to say next. Malik turned the engine on, having to get away from the hospital. He headed towards home, wanting to be with his mother and Trinity. Then it occurred to him to swing by the stash house for no other reason than to look around. He wondered where exactly Roxanne was shot up. He had a suspicion that Roxanne hd been at the stash house. Nisha would have known more if that were not the case.

The block was quiet, yet with an eerie feeling; like the calm after a storm. He slowed down as he neared the stash house in the middle of the block. He pulled to the curb, parking, realizing it was the first time here that he'd not pulled into the backyard with a trunk full of cocaine.

In the night he could hardly tell that there'd been much foot activity except for the discarded latex gloves strewn along the driveway. The front door was closed, yellow crime scene tape hanging from its edges.

He walked slowly, looking towards the backyard. The back of Roxanne's Maxima was visible. His heart sank, imagining the scene, knowing now that it was Hill and Shoota. He suspected that Hill must have killed Shoota and dumped him behind Ralph's grocery market.

There was one more thing to check. He rounded the back of the house. The back porch light was on. The concrete was stained with blood. The bushes surrounding the porch had been trampled upon. On the ground there appeared to be thick pours of detergent, but Malik knew that it was cocaine.

Inside the house, bloody footprints led the way from the back door. The walls were smeared with blood, the hands as if struggling to hold on. Blood stained the white carpeting, leading to the living room. The hallway walls were riddled with bullets.

Malik caught his breath when he turned to the dining room table. Cocaine was spilled from a ceramic plate across the table and onto the carpet, covering the deep red pooled blood. He imagined this was where she was when they entered the house.

Malik checked the front room. The closet where he'd stashed the twenty kilos for Roxanne was empty except for tossed duffel bags. He leaned against the cool wall, closing his eyes against the deadly scene. Tears pushed against his eyelids, forcing their way through at the corners.

Malik departed the stash house with a red hot fire burning inside for revenge. He tore away from the curb and headed to the only place he knew to possibly find Hill; Crenshaw Boulevard.

The large pistol was cold in his lap as he drove down Florence Avenue, catching green lights all the way, taking this as a sign that his mission was right. His body tingled with the certainty of what he was set out to do. He'd never shot anyone.

The street got brighter the closer he got to Crenshaw. The cars got slower as they cruised by, looking, observing, checking, and remembering the drivers and cars they passed.

Malik was looking for one specific car. He was looking for that ominous black Cadillac with its tail jacked in the air. The driver would have on a baseball cap turned to the back. There might be two.

The Shell gas station on the corner of Florence and Crenshaw was lit up, its bright lights like disco balls for the smiling, joking, observant people cruising through and parked near the pumps. Malik scanned the small groups carefully, sure that he was making some nervous, them not knowing what his intentions were. He remembered seeing a man get shot and jacked for his Mustang 5.0 the last time he was there with Shoota.

The Cadillac was not at the Shell gas station. He continued down Crenshaw. The opposite lane was cleared for two low-riders as they passed by hitting switches, their front ends jumping in tandem high in the air.

Glamorous low-riders followed, their passengers hanging out the windows, cheering excitedly. Malik looked to the far side of the street, along the block-long wall mural, half expecting to see Freeway Rick and his crew, but there was no sign of Hill or his menacing Cadillac.

A police car sidled up next to Malik at the red light of Vernon, essentially the end of the Crenshaw strip. Malik imagined that the officer saw a square in a square's car. He silently thanked Elisa for her taste in clothes. He waited for the pig to make a right on Vernon, fully suspecting he'd make his way back around.

Malik didn't want to be seen by the pig again. Just as he prepared to head home, resolving to find Hill another day he suddenly remembered Shoota taking him to Hill's house. He remembered that it was in the 60s off West Boulevard, but not the exact cross street.

He remembered landmarks though, making a left on Vernon and deciding to head up West B. until he recognized the corner he should turn down. He remembered it was right after a blue sign welcoming people to the city of Inglewood.

Malik gripped both the .44 Magnum and the steering wheel as he cruised observantly up West Boulevard, passing through the 50s and slowing when he got to the 60s, looking for the welcome sign to Inglewood.

He almost missed the sign in the night, slowing to make sure it was the one he remembered seeing. He drove slowly to the next street, looking down the quiet residential block for any familiar cars or houses. Nothing was familiar.

The next corner he remembered. It was a shallow dirt yard. He remembered how different it was from the previous corner, as if marking the true welcome mat for the city of Inglewood.

Malik made a right and cruised to the next street, remembering the steep dip in the street. The mix of shabby and well cared for houses reminded him of where he should be heading. The dirt yard came up suddenly, Hill's house leaning back from the street. His stomach turned at the sight of the Cadillac parked deep into the driveway, only it wasn't black; it was a gold color.

The next street was dark and quiet. Malik parked near the corner to prevent any chance of being blocked in. He sat in silence, looking to the house he was parked in front of, noticing it was the side. The front door must've been around the corner, he reasoned.

His hands sweat on the cool pearl handle of the pistol. He had no idea how to proceed. *Just go,* he whispered to himself, taking a deep breath.

He had no idea he was sweating until the cool night air met the sheen on his face. He walked deliberately up the street, his heart beating faster the closer he got to the dirt front lawn of Hill's house.

Oddly, he felt safer when he turned into the yard, skirting along the side of the cool steel of the Cadillac towards the backyard. He suspected that Hill's bedroom might be in back. He was thinking to peer into the windows for any sign of him when he heard voices.

He'd never considered looking inside the garage. It looked like no one would dare spend time under its crumbling frame. The rotten wooden double doors were chained together. A small slice of light shined through a top crease of the door frame.

Malik licked his lips nervously, the large pistol hanging to his side as he crept to the edge of the garage. The voices were more distinct. Hill was inside. It sounded like his brother was with him. There was a side door further along the side of the garage. Malik reached the door. He pressed his face to an opening. Hill and his brother, Al, stood facing each other on either side of a foldable card table. On top of the table were the twenty kilos Malik had left for Roxanne.

Al chuckled. "You did it this time," he said, passing a smoking joint across the table to Hill.

"On sixties, cuz, that nigga was beggin'," said Hill, his yellow face eery under the lone hanging lightbulb. "The bitch was more gangsta than him."

"I can't believe she didn't hit you."

Hill grinned, exhaling a long plume of marijuana smoke. "That nigga stepped out there first," he said.

Malik clenched his teeth. He gripped the pistol tight and took a deep breath of the cool night air. He slowly touched the rusted handle of the door.

With one swift motion Malik snatched open the door. Hill and Al looked up, startled. The spark of the big pistol accompanied the big bang, snatching Malik's wrist.

Hill's chest exploded red as he was thrown back to the far wall.

Malik followed a scrambling Al, the blast following him over a chair, ripping through the back of his head.

Malik stood still, the new quiet replacing the loud bangs of the pistol. He breathed heavily, the dead bodies laying at odd angles; Hill's eyes staring up at him across the dusty space.

Chapter Thirty-Nine

Dancing With Devils

It wasn't until Malik pulled to a stop in his driveway, into the spot his grandfather's Lincoln would usually occupy, that he felt his breath. He killed the motor and inhaled deeply. It was only now that he regretted not hurriedly grabbing the twenty kilos of cocaine off the card table. The large pistol lay like a deadly snake on the seat next to him. He couldn't decide what to do with it. It smelled like hot metal. He could still see the damage the bullets did as they tore through flesh and bone.

He stepped from the car, holding the gun loosely as he

looked to the street. He listened for the sound of sirens. The night was quiet and still. He grabbed a backpack of money and the portable phone from the car.

Trinity was waiting for him, appearing at the bedroom door when he entered the house. She rushed to him, wrapping her arms around him.

"Are you okay?" she asked, looking to his face, searching for the night's events in his eyes.

"I'm good," he replied huskily. "Mom cool?"

Trinity nodded, walking with him to the bedroom, never taking her arms from around him.

Malik silently turned her to him once they were in the bedroom. He kissed her softly, needing her sweet touch after the sour night. His lips hungrily searched her mouth, trapping her tongue with his lips. He sucked the tender flesh, gripping her plump ass in the process.

Trinity moaned under his aggressive touch. She accepted his unquestioned hunger. She folded to his touch, allowing his strong hands to shed her clothes. His emotion was contagious.

Malik was filled with a burning desire to devour Trinity. He ignored her tender resistance to his aggressive touch. He didn't hear her question him about what was going on with him.

Trinity bent for him, taking him inside her from the back. His powerful thrusts moved her forward while his strong grip brought her back to him. She whispered under the assault, taking all of his powerful emotion inside of her.

Malik lost himself, slamming into her with wild abandon. He didn't hear her call his name. He didn't hear her plea to slow down. He didn't hear her cries until he exploded inside of her and collapsed on her back.

* * *

Be careful, baby, Malik heard his mother say even now as he announced himself at The Law Offices Of Saul Benjamin.

Saul was smiling behind his desk as Malik entered. "Look at this guy," he said, looking to Joseph Mordecai seated in a far corner.

"Glad to meet you," said Malik, shaking the blue-eyed man's dry hand.

"Sorry about your friend, Shoota," said Joseph.

"Right on," replied Malik, sitting in the leather chair before the smiling Saul.

"So you know," Saul began, "we're here for whatever you need." He nodded, looking to Joseph quickly.

"We're a team," said Joseph. "It's your call though."

"We hope Roxanne wakes up and makes a full recovery," added Saul, smiling. "But the best we can do for her is to continue with business."

"A bigger, better business," interjected Joseph.

Malik didn't trust Saul. He waited for them to ask for the connection to Mario, but they didn't. He was glad because he'd hate to have to deny them.

Keeping Mario private is what Roxanne would want, Malik said to himself, hoping she awakened soon to wipe the silly smile off of Saul's fat face.

Nothing will ever be the same for Malik Toole.

Peter Mack speaks on it:

Greetings, beautiful people. I'd like to thank you for sharing this experience with me. I'd like to thank Joy Deja King for the opportunity to share her vision for the Coke Series. It was fun visiting my youth. The people and places are true. Los Angeles in the '80s was a wild west for cocaine and new money.

Next we'll be in the '90s. Malik's sons have come of age to wage war in the streets and learn for the first time that they are brothers.

A KING PRODUCTION

MEN OF
The Bitch Series
AND THE WOMEN WHO
Love Them

JOY DEJA KING

Chapter One

Adrenaline Rush

Before Precious Cummings stole their hearts, there was another woman both Nico Carter and Supreme shared. But until this day, they never knew it. Her name was Vandresse Lawson and although she loved them both, she was only in love with herself and it cost her everything.

"Girl, that color is poppin'. I think I need to get that too," Tanica said, eyeing her friend's nail polish as the Chinese lady was polishing them.

"You bet not! We ain't gon' be walking around here wit' the same color polish on," Vandresse huffed.

"Won't nobody be paying attention to that shit," Tanica said, sucking her teeth.

"Stop it!" Vandresse frowned up her face as if. "You know everybody around here pay attention to what I do. All these chicks dying to be just like me," she boasted, admiring how the plum polish made her honey-colored skin pop.

Tanica glanced over at her best friend and rolled her eyes. She loved Vandresse like a sister, but at the same time Tanica felt she was so full of shit. But there was no denying, in the streets of Harlem: Vandresse was the queen of this shit. She was always the real pretty girl in the neighborhood, but once she started fuckin' with that nigga Courtney, it was on. Nobody could tell her nothing, including her childhood friend Tanica.

"I'll take that pink color," Tanica told the lady doing her nails. She had no desire to beef with Vandresse over something as simple as polish. "So are we going to the club tonight or what?" she asked ready to talk about having some fun.

"I can't." Vandresse sighed.

"Why not? We've been talking about hitting this club since we first heard they was reopening it weeks ago."

"I know, but I told Courtney we would hang out tonight."

"Ya always hang out. Can't you spend a little time with your best friend?"

"Maybe tomorrow. I mean look at this tennis bracelet he got me." Vandresse held up her arm and slowly twirled her wrist like she was waving in a beauty pageant. "These diamonds are stunning. If I have to spend some quality time wit' my man, give him some head, sex him real good so the gifts keep coming, you gotta understand that," Vandresse explained with no filter as if the nail salon wasn't full of people, but of course she didn't give a fuck.

"I get it. I just miss hanging out with you. Brittany is cool, but she's not as fun as you," Tanica hated to admit.

"Of course she isn't, but it's not her fault. I'm the turn up queen." Vandresse laughed.

"Yeah you are." Tanica joined in on the laugh.

"But on the real. I miss hanging out with you too even though we're roommates and attend hair school together. But we haven't just hung out and had some fun like we used to. I wish Courtney had a cute friend I could hook you up with."

"Me too. Because that one you hooked me up with last time was not the answer."

"I know, but I was hoping his money would help you excuse his face," Vandresse said shrugging.

"How you luck out and get a dude who's cute and got money," Tanica stated shaking her head. "I can't believe out of all the friends Courtney got ain't none of them good looking."

"That's not true. One of his friends is a real cutie, but he just a low level worker. But he can afford to take you out to eat and buy you some sneakers... stuff like that. At least we would be able to do some double dating. If you want me to hook you up just say the word."

"Let me think about it. I don't know if I wanna sit around watching yo' man shower you wit' diamonds, all while homeboy taking me to Footlocker, so I can pick out a new pair of Nikes."

"You so crazy." Vandresse giggled before both girls burst out laughing while continuing to chat and make jokes while finishing up at the nail salon.

"I figured you would wanna chill tonight," Vandresse said looking in the passenger side mirror as she put on some more lip gloss. "I did say I was gonna treat you extra special tonight for icing out my wrist so lovely." She smiled, using the tip of her freshly manicured nail to tap the diamonds on her tennis bracelet.

"I didn't forget. I'ma hold you to that." Courtney winked, squeezing Vandresse's bare upper thigh. "But umm, I told my man Anton I would stop by for a second. He poppin' some bottles for his birthday. Nothing major. He keepin' low key. But we do a lot of business together and I promised I come through."

"I feel you." Vandresse smiled not really caring either way. She was already plotting on how she was going to suck his dick so good tonight so she could get a diamond ring to go with her bracelet.

"But when we leave here, it's back to the crib so you can take care of Daddy." Courtney nodded.

"You know I got you, baby." Vandresse licked her lips thinking how lucky she was to have a sexy nigga who could fuck and was getting money out in these streets.

When they walked into the Uptown lounge it was jammed pack. "I thought you said this was low key," Vandresse commented.

"A lot of niggas fuck wit' Anton so they all probably coming through to show love," Courtney replied as he headed straight to the back like he knew exactly where he was going. Vandresse was right by his side, happy that she decided to wear a sexy dress tonight since there was a gang of chicks in the spot. When it came to stuntin' on other bitches, Vandresse was super competitive. She always wanted to be number one or at the very least top three.

"My nigga, C!" A guy who Vandresse assumed was the birthday boy stood up showing Courtney love.

"Happy birthday, man!" Courtney grinned. "I see everybody came out to show love to my homie."

"Yeah, I wasn't expecting all these people, but hey it's my birthday! You and your lady sit down and have some champagne," Anton said, playing the perfect host.

Courtney took Vandresse's hand so they could sit down. "Baby, I'll be right back. I need to go to the restroom. Have a glass of bubbly waiting for me when I get back," she said kissing him on the cheek.

"Excuse me, where's the restroom?" Vandresse asked one of the cocktail waitresses. The lady pointed up the stairs so Vandresse headed in that direction.

When she got to the bathroom, Vandresse was relieved nobody was in there. She wanted to check to make sure one of her tracks hadn't came loose. Vandresse always kept a needle and some thread in her purse just in case. She examined her weave and to her relief it wasn't a loose track brushing against her ear, it was her leave out.

Vandresse glanced at her reflection one last time and after feeling confident she had her shit together, she exited out right as a handful of chicks were coming in.

Right in the entry way of the bathroom there was a huge spotlight. When Vandresse came in, the upstairs was damn near empty, but when she came out, there were a ton of people and all eyes seemed to be fixated on her. *Thank goodness I made sure I was straight before I walked out*, Vandresse thought to herself. She was heading back down stairs when she felt a firm grasp on her arm.

"Why the fu..." before Vandresse had a chance to curse the man out, she locked eyes with a nigga so fine she changed her mind.

"I apologize for grabbing on you, but I couldn't let you get away. You are beautiful. What's your name?"

"Vandresse," she uttered. The man's intense stare had her feeling self-conscious for some reason. Like his eyes were piercing through her soul.

"My name is Nico. Nico Carter. Come sit down with me so we can have a drink." He spoke with so much confidence that Vandresse found herself following behind the stranger like her man wasn't downstairs waiting for her.

"I'm sorry. I can't go with you," she finally said, snapping out of her trance.

"No need to apologize. Did I do or say something to offend you?" Nico questioned.

"Not at all. I'm actually here with my man. He's downstairs waiting for me."

"Oh, really," Nico said unmoved. "That might be a problem for you tonight, but it doesn't have to be tomorrow."

Vandresse gave Nico a quizzical look. "I'm not following you."

"You're not wearing a wedding ring so you not married. Are you willing to miss out on what might be the best thing that ever happened to you?"

"Wow, you're a little full of yourself."

"Only because I have every reason to be. Give me your phone number. I'm more of an action person than a talker."

Vandresse wanted to say no because she had a good thing going with Courtney, but she also knew it wasn't a sure thing. Like Nico said, he wasn't her husband and they were both young. Vandresse wasn't stupid. She was well aware Courtney was still out there doing him. Vandresse knew she was his main bitch, but not his only chick.

"Here," she said, writing her number on a napkin then handing it to Nico.

"You're smart and beautiful. I think we'll get along just fine."

"We shall see. But I gotta go."

"Cool, I'll call you tomorrow." Nico stood at the top of the stairs looking over the banister and watched Vandresse walk over to a small group of people. A young dude stood up and took her hand and he figured that must be her man. Nico knew he needed to leave that alone, but the same way he got an adrenaline rush from dealing drugs, chasing a beautiful woman that was technically unavailable gave Nico that same high.

P.O. Box 912
Collierville, TN 38027

www.joydejaking.com
www.twitter.com/joydejaking

A King Production

ORDER FORM

Name:

Address:

City/State:

Zip:

QUANTITY	TITLES	PRICE	TOTAL
	Bitch	$15.00	
	Bitch Reloaded	$15.00	
	The Bitch Is Back	$15.00	
	Queen Bitch	$15.00	
	Last Bitch Standing	$15.00	
	Superstar	$15.00	
	Ride Wit' Me	$12.00	
	Ride Wit' Me Part 2	$15.00	
	Stackin' Paper	$15.00	
	Trife Life To Lavish	$15.00	
	Trife Life To Lavish II	$15.00	
	Stackin' Paper II	$15.00	
	Rich or Famous	$15.00	
	Rich or Famous Part 2	$15.00	
	Rich or Famous Part 3	$15.00	
	Bitch A New Beginning	$15.00	
	Mafia Princess Part 1	$15.00	
	Mafia Princess Part 2	$15.00	
	Mafia Princess Part 3	$15.00	
	Mafia Princess Part 4	$15.00	
	Mafia Princess Part 5	$15.00	
	Boss Bitch	$15.00	
	Baller Bitches Vol. 1	$15.00	
	Baller Bitches Vol. 2	$15.00	
	Baller Bitches Vol. 3	$15.00	
	Bad Bitch	$15.00	
	Still The Baddest Bitch	$15.00	
	Power	$15.00	
	Power Part 2	$15.00	
	Drake	$15.00	
	Drake Part 2	$15.00	
	Female Hustler	$15.00	
	Female Hustler Part 2	$15.00	
	Female Hustler Part 3	$15.00	
	Princess Fever "Birthday Bash"	$9.99	
	Nico Carter The Men Of The Bitch Series	$15.00	
	Bitch The Beginning Of The End	$15.00	
	Supreme...Men Of The Bitch Series	$15.00	
	Bitch The Final Chapter	$15.00	
	Stackin' Paper III	$15.00	
	Men Of The Bitch Series And The Women Who Love Them	$15.00	
	Coke Like The 80s	$15.00	

Shipping/Handling (Via Priority Mail) $6.50 1-2 Books, $8.95 3-4 Books add $1.95 for ea. Additional book.

Total: $_____**FORMS OF ACCEPTED PAYMENTS:** Certified or government issued checks and money Orders, all mail in orders take 5-7 Business days to be delivered